Yoga for Prosperity

ENRICH YOUR LIFE THROUGH
KUNDALINI YOGA & MEDITATION
AS TAUGHT BY YOGI BHAJAN, PH.D

by
Siri Kirpal Kaur Khalsa

YOGI JI PRESS, NEW MEXICO

Published and Distributed by:
Yogi Ji Press
PO Box 970, Santa Cruz, NM 87567
Tel:(505)753-5086
E-mail:nam@newmexico.com

KRI Seal of Approval:
This Seal of Approval is granted only to those products
which have been approved through the KRI Review process
for accuracy and integrity of those portions which embody
the technology of Kundalini Yoga and 3HO Lifestyle as
taught by Yogi Bhajan

Disclaimer
This book draws on ancient wisdom from the East and West. The technologies
described are effective when practiced accurately. This information is not meant
to replace medical treatment where indicated. Results may vary. Please consult
your physician before starting any new physical exercise program.

GREEN AND GOLD SONG

by Siri Kirpal Kaur Khalsa (& God)
November 28, 2001

The Earth sings its green and gold song
to the vastness of the heavens,
And the heavens beam back an illuminating answer
that gilds all lives with sunlit glory.

No one would count the drops of water in the sea,
And God's leaves of grass are more numerous than
Whitman's.

Reality is abundant, vast and Infinite,
the endless giving of the endless Creator.
There is no lack. Scarcity is a lie.

ACKNOWLEDGEMENTS

First and foremost, I am deeply grateful to God for manifesting this book through me and also for creating everyone else on this list.

This book would not have been possible without my spiritual teacher, Siri Singh Sahib Bhai Sahib Harbhajan Singh Khalsa Yogiji, better known as Yogi Bhajan. He was the first person to openly teach Kundalini Yoga, which he brought to the West in 1969 and which he has shared fearlessly and unstintingly ever since. His teachings have been the inspiration for many prosperous enterprises as well as a source of upliftment for many. I am deeply grateful for his presence in my life and for the wealth of knowledge he has shared.

Thanks go to MSS Tarn Taran Singh Khalsa and S.S. Tarn Taran Kaur Khalsa for sharing the story of the Yogi Tea Company and to Simran Kaur Khalsa Wester of 3HO Deutschland for information on the current state of Kundalini Yoga in Germany.

I am grateful to SS Viriam Singh Khalsa for organizing the Northwest Kundalini Yoga Teachers Conferences, one of which provided the impetus for this book. I am also grateful to Darshan Kaur Khalsa of the Dasvandh Office for suggesting I write the articles that proved to be the warm-up exercises for this book. Thanks go to Tej Kaur Khalsa and Diane Bunting (Shamsher Kaur) for help with documentation.

I am grateful to Simrat Kaur Khalsa for her illustrations and for proceeding despite camera problems. Thanks go to the people who gave their time to model specifically for this book: Gurunam Kaur Atwal, Strawberry Gatts, Tamar Hurwitz, Dorene Steggell, Lexy Wellman, Harinder K.Khalsa, Ardas Kaur Khalsa, and Daryl Thomas;. and to Yoga West in Eugene, OR for letting us use their space.

A special thanks goes to Thomas Gorski who took the picture of me on the back cover on very short notice.

And I am deeply grateful for my husband, who gives me love, support, encouragement, help with library research, and much help with the computer.

FORWARD

by Fred Brown

To see through the eyes of Spirit is the key to finding prosperity. So many people look at prosperity as a state of outer wealth. Actually it is a state of inner wealth that comes from a deep sense of understanding that the universe will take care of us if we only apply love, patience, kindness, generosity, and all the other fruits of the Spirit to our material life. The inner fulfillment one creates from following this path generates the outer fulfillment we need to live in this world.

Life flows, and if we are flowing in Spirit with it, all our needs will be met. That is the essence of Prosperity. The challenge is to find your path to this serene state. Siri Kirpal has given you many excellent ways to follow. I hope you will take them.

Fred Brown has been a Personal Financial Consultant/Therapist for over 28 years and has five books published on Personal Finance including two on Money and Spirit. Currently he writes a "Money and Spirit" column for the Santa Fe New Mexican. Recently he was included with a pantheon of well known advisors, including Sir Thomas More, and Peter Drucker in a book entitled "Clients for Life: How Great Professionals Develop Breakthrough Relationships," (Simon Schuster 2000)

DEDICATED

to Gregory Neil Beretta
because I once made a promise,
and to James Michael Waldon
who has husbanded both me and this book

Siri Kirpal Kaur Khalsa

AUTHOR'S PREFACE

Like many people, I used to believe that spiritual people could not be prosperous; that prosperous people would have a hard time being spiritual. Now I understand that spiritual people are so connected to the Source of everything that spiritual people are the most prosperous people of all. Furthermore, a prosperous person has what it takes to give, so a truly prosperous person has what it takes to be very spiritual.

The change in my thinking came about over a fairly lengthy period of time. In 1987, my spiritual teacher, Yogi Bhajan, looked at me and said as if he were thinking out loud, "Poverty is not a blessing, but a curse." That same year, a fellow astrologer looked over my chart and said that I had once made a vow of poverty and had taken it so seriously that it was causing problems in this life and that the only way to change the pattern was "to take a vow of wealth." These two statements got me thinking, but it took awhile for me to make any serious changes or to even seriously investigate the wealth of yogic material on prosperity.

The next change came in 1994 when I realized that by learning and using prosperity meditations and other yogic techniques for prosperity I would be a better teacher for my Kundalini Yoga students who were struggling financially. So, I tried them and discovered that prosperity meditations bring joy to the heart and mind. They are wonderful to do just for the fun of it even if prosperity is not an issue. By 2000, I realized that I had enough information on prosperity for a book and that it would be an act of kindness to make these techniques available to the general public.

As I was typing the manuscript of this book, the World Trade Center and the Pentagon were attacked. After the initial shock, as I was still reeling with the horror of it, I began to wonder if it was really relevant to publish a yoga book for prosperity at a time like this. Then it dawned on me: it is exactly the qualities that lead to prosperity that also allow us to survive with our humanity intact even when "all hell is breaking loose" seems like an understatement. A positive attitude, an open heart, the willingness to reach out to others, being at the right place at the right time, and coming through all obstacles with radiant success are exactly the qualities we need right now...and these are exactly the qualities that make for prosperity. Several of the techniques in this book are also techniques for protection.

The people who are happiest at times like these are those who meditate, those who reach out to others in service, those who follow the call of their souls, those who keep their hearts open. These qualities keep us from collapse in deadly times, and these same qualities bring us prosperity.

May you learn these techniques so that you have the power to give. May you empower yourself so that you can empower others. May you be kind to yourself so that you can be kind to all creation. May God shower you with all blessings.

By the Grace of God,
Siri Kirpal Kaur Khalsa
Salem OR USA

TABLE OF CONTENTS

Yoga for Prosperity

INTRODUCTION TO KUNDALINI YOGA, MEDITATION, AND SHABAD YOGA

"Gratitude is the open door to abundance." Yogi Bhajan

This book is intended to be used by anyone - by people who have never done Kundalini Yoga and people who teach Kundalini Yoga; by people who are financially challenged and people who make millions of dollars a year. Anyone can benefit from using this book. Many of the meditations and *shabads* are personal favorites of mine that I have practiced regularly over a period of time.

There are several ways of using this book. It is designed so that you can use it as a course of study on prosperity yoga, trying out the techniques chapter by chapter. This makes it useful for teachers who plan to give courses in Kundalini Yoga for prosperity. It also makes it useful if you plan to do your own course of study or want to learn the techniques thoroughly. Another way to use the book is to flip through the pages and find a practice that meets your personal situation. For instance, if you are facing serious challenges, you may wish to practice

This chapter is a guide to using the techniques in this book. We will look at ways you can use the book, how to tune in (very important!), how to design a personal practice or *sadhana*, why relaxation is important, and how to conclude a deep relaxation. We will examine the basics of meditation and common misconceptions about meditation, and the basics of *shabad yoga*. A pronunciation guide and pointers for practice are also included.

1

the Meditation to Tap Opportunities or one of the meditations in the chapter on the Radiant Body. If you greatly desire some specific thing, you might find the Beggar's Meditation useful. On the other hand, if you are simply feeling dissatisfaction with your life, one of the techniques in the Spirit of Prosperity chapter might be just what you're looking for.

In any event, if you are new to Kundalini Yoga, please review the basic information in this chapter and the chapter on breathing before jumping into your practice. Classes taught by a KRI certified teacher can give you invaluable hands-on experience, as well as the blessings of group energy. The website for locating KRI certified teachers is listed in the Resources section of this book.

TUNING IN

First, always tune in. Because Kundalini Yoga is one of the most powerful forms of yoga that can be taught on a daily basis, we need to do it in the presence of a master. We do that by "tuning in," chanting a mantra which aligns us with the past and present master teachers of this discipline and helps us drop our ego attachments.

To tune in, sit in a comfortable cross-legged position or, if this is difficult, in a chair with the feet flat on the ground. Sit very straight and regally with the chin tucked in just a bit so that the neck is in line with the rest of the spine. Place the palms together as for prayer at the center of the chest where you can feel your sternum bone. Close the eyes. Focus attention at the brow point, which is centered between the eyes and a bit above them. You may inhale once or twice to center yourself. Then inhale to begin and chant *Ong Naamo Guroo Dayv Naamo* at least three times, preferably on a single breath for each repetition. *Dayv* is chanted a minor third higher than the rest of the mantra.

This mantra may be translated, "I call upon the Creator. I call upon Divine Wisdom."

Immediately after chanting *Ong Naamo,* you may also chant *Aad Guray Nameh, Jugaad Guray Nameh, Sat Guray Nameh, Siri Guroo Dayvay Nameh* also for three times or more, also preferably on a single breath for each repetition.

This second mantra creates a protective field. It may be translated, "I call upon the primal wisdom. I call upon the wisdom of the ages. I call upon the true wisdom. I call upon the infinitely great divine wisdom."

How to Design a Personal Spiritual Practice

There are many ways of designing a personal sadhana or spiritual practice. A good format consists of tuning in, yogic warm-ups, a Kundalini Yoga set, deep relaxation and meditation for 11 minutes or more, followed by prayer, song, or inspirational reading. You may start with much less, such as tuning in followed by just 3 minutes of meditation. I assure you that any positive effort you make will bring positive results.

Prosperity meditations are usually most effective if practiced 120 days or more. It takes 40 days to change an old habit. It takes 90 days to establish a new habit. It takes 120 days to lock the new habit into the subconscious so that it becomes automatic. It takes 1000 days (nearly 3 years) to master a new habit. It is thus a good idea to pick a meditation or shabad that meets your needs and practice it daily for 40, 90, 120, or 1000 days. Kundalini Yoga sets may be rotated on a daily basis or practiced for 40 days or more.

The ideal time for this practice is in the early morning between 4:00 a.m. and 7:00 a.m. This period of time is ordinarily free of distractions, prepares us for the upcoming day, and has the perfect vibration for meditation as this is the time the pituitary is most active. Some people, including me, enjoy meditating in the evening before bed as well. (This is not the best time for Breath of Fire!) Some people prefer to do their spiritual practice after work before dinner. Both the *Meditation for Gurprasaad* and the *Meditation for Prosperity and Self-Esteem* are easy, quiet, and short enough to be done sitting at a desk during a work break.

The standard sitting position for meditation and many yoga exercises is Easy Pose, a simple cross-legged position. Nearly anything that is done in Easy Pose can also be done sitting in a chair with both feet flat on the ground and the weight evenly balanced between them. Another common posture is Rock Pose. This is done by sitting on the heels with the spine straight. If sitting on the heels is difficult for you, you may substitute Easy Pose or sitting in a chair instead, or use a pillow under your buttocks.

Some of the Kundalini Yoga sets given in this book are very easy and may be done without warming up the spine first, notably the *Basic Spinal Energy Set*. Other sets should only be done after a good yogic warm-up, notably the *Set for the Navel Center*. It is acceptable to practice individual exercises separate from sets for this purpose. Exercises that are especially suitable for warm-ups include Spinal Flexes, Spinal Twists, Cat-Cow and Life Nerve Stretch. Start with exercises that stretch the lower part of the body and work your way up. It is also acceptable to use a warm-up sequence from another yogic tradition before practicing a Kundalini Yoga set.

RELAXATION

The art of relaxation is an important part of Kundalini Yoga. It is also an important part of prosperity. In both cases, relaxation is the art of allowing the work we have done to consolidate and become effective.

Unless otherwise specified, it is optimal to relax and circulate the energy for a minute or two after each exercise. You may relax on the back or on the stomach or in a sitting position depending on the exercise you've just done. It's fine, especially in the morning, to shorten or dispense with these relaxation times to avoid falling asleep. It is also acceptable to increase the relaxation times if you are a beginner or the exercise was unusually strenuous.

At the end of a set, we relax deeply on the back with the arms by the sides and the palms facing up. The legs are out straight, and the ankles do not cross. Let go of any tension. This position is called corpse pose. You may cover yourself with a natural fiber blanket or quilt during the deep relaxation. It is pleasant (but optional) to play meditative music. Suitable tapes and CDs with a prosperity focus are available through the Resources listed in the back.

Bring yourself back from the deep relaxation at the end of the set in the following way:

1. Inhale and exhale deeply. Consciously bring yourself back.

2. Still lying on the back, rotate the ankles and wrists in small circles. Continue for 10-15 seconds. Then reverse the direction and continue for another 10-15 seconds.

3. Cat Stretch: Leaving both shoulders on the ground, stretch one leg over the other, first on one side and then on the other. Both arms may be stretched out to the side on the ground, or the arm on the side with the moving leg may be stretched overhead on the ground.

4.Lying on the back, rub the palms together and the bottoms of the feet together. Continue for 10-15 seconds
5.Bring the knees to the chest and wrap the arms around the legs. Roll back and forth on the spine several times. Then roll up into a sitting position and prepare to meditate or conclude the practice.

MEDITATION BASICS

There are several misconceptions about meditation. The most common misconception is that meditation involves stopping the mind from thinking. This isn't possible. Our minds are designed to produce thoughts. Think of a clear stream and a polluted stream. A polluted stream is not likely to have many fish in it, and those fish it does have are likely to be unhealthy. A clear stream is likely to have more fish, and those fish will tend to be healthier. Our minds are like those streams. A clear mind will have healthier thoughts than a polluted mind has, and it will be easier to access them. So, in meditation, we simply allow our thoughts to exist, without attaching to them, and without reacting. When we let go, there comes a point where the mind feels very quiet because we aren't reacting to our thoughts. If you do react to your thoughts, don't react to your reaction. Simply get back to the meditation.

Another common misconception about meditation is that it's going to be blissful. The divine light is in all of us. To access that light we need to clean the windows of our minds on a regular basis. That is what meditation is for. But, you know, I've never met a person yet who considers window cleaning one of their favorite activities. So if you find yourself crying, getting angry, reliving a hurtful experience when you were age five, you're not doing it wrong. This doesn't mean you should wallow in negativity during meditation. Just keep meditating and be grateful for the opportunity to release the pain. Eventually, it will disappear. Meditation is mental elbow grease that makes bliss possible.

Many meditations involve the use of a mantra. A mantra is a repeated sound that alters the mind and consciousness. Chanting a mantra out loud activates positive change, releases hidden potentials, and stimulates the centers of the brain that create the experience of God-consciousness or Universal awareness. When we chant a mantra either silently or out loud, we are focusing on a positive, divine sound that cuts through the negativity of the subconscious mind.

In most cases, meditation times are specified; in some cases, times are open. Common practice times are 3 minutes, 11 minutes, 22 minutes, 31 minutes, 62 minutes and 2 1/2 hours. Positive changes to the glandular system begin after 3 minutes of practice. The pituitary and nervous system are stimulated with 11 minutes of practice. The three mental bodies come into balance with 22 minutes of practice. The whole mind, the aura, and the elements associated with the lower five chakras come into balance with 31 minutes of practice. The inner self and outer projection come into balance with 62 minutes of practice. And 2 1/2 hours of practice holds the benefits throughout the day. This final benefit accrues to all spiritual practice you do through any given day

The eye focus is specified in most meditations. Where it is not specified, you have a choice. The most common eye focus is to close the eyes and focus at the brow point, which is centered between the eyes and slightly above them. This stimulates the pituitary and intuition. Another common eye focus is to look down at the tip of the nose without crossing the eyes. This helps control the mind. It is also possible to close the eyes and focus at the top of the head, which stimulates the pineal gland and the *crown chakra*. Another possible focus is to keep the eyes 1/10th open and focus either at the brow point or on the tip of the nose. This stimulates the *sixth chakra*. It is possible to close the eyes and focus down to the center of the chin. This enhances our connection to our core self. And finally, it is possible to leave the eyes mostly open and stare straight ahead with a soft gaze.

MUDRAS

A mudra is a hand position. The following mudras may be used when no other mudra is specified. The first four mudras are commonly done with the hands or wrists on the knees.

Gyan Mudra: This is the most common mudra used. Touch the tip of the thumb to the tip of the index finger (Jupiter finger). This is the passive form of Gyan Mudra and stimulates knowledge, wisdom, and receptivity. You may also curl the index finger under the thumb so that the fingernail of the index finger touches the joint of the thumb. This is the active form of Gyan Mudra and has the same effects, but in a more projective, active way.

Shuni Mudra - Touch the tip of the thumb to the tip of the middle finger (Saturn finger). This stimulates the capacities for patience, self-discipline, and commitment.

Surya Mudra - Touch the tip of the thumb to the tip of the ring finger (Sun finger). This stimulates health, rejuvenation, and creativity.

Buddhi Mudra - Touch the tip of the thumb to the tip of the little finger (Mercury finger). This stimulates prosperity, friendship, and effective communication.

Prayer Mudra - This is the mudra we use for tuning in. Place the palms flat together. Usually we place this mudra at the heart center touching the sternum. This mudra balances the hemispheres of the brain. It is commonly used for prayer and devotion.

Venus Lock - This mudra is used in many Kundalini Yoga exercises. It helps channel sexual energy and promotes glandular balance. Used in meditation, it improves focus and concentration. Women interlace the fingers with the right little finger on the bottom. The right thumb goes on webbing between the left thumb and index finger. The left thumb is on top and presses the fleshy mound (the mound of Venus) at the base of the right thumb. Men reverse the direction of all fingers so that the right thumb is on top and left little finger is on the bottom.

Hands in the Lap - Men place the right hand on top of the left with the palms facing up and the thumbs touching. Women reverse the direction. This creates a state of meditative receptivity. For the same effect, it's also possible to interlace the fingers with the palms facing up with the thumbs either touching or separated.

SHABAD YOGA: WHAT IT IS, WHY IT WORKS, HOW TO DO IT

Shabad yoga is a powerful yogic technique and one of my favorite techniques, especially for prosperity. You can think of shabads (divine poetry), as extended mantras. They work exactly the way mantras do. As with mantras, reciting shabads in the original *Gurmukhi* language creates a neuro-chemical effect in the brain that produces a profound impact on consciousness. As with mantras, reciting shabads creates a positive sound and thought that cuts through the negativity that lurks in the subconscious. For this reason, shabads work most effectively when sung or recited in the original Gurmukhi as meditations in their own right. My students and I have also used shabads successfully as affirmations recited in English.

There are a couple of differences in the way we practice mantras and the way we practice shabads. First, with mantras it is optional to cover the head during practice; with shabads it is not. Shabad yoga is an extremely powerful technique. The impact the practice of shabads in the original Gurmukhi makes on the consciousness is so great that the head should be covered, preferably with white cotton, to provide insulation.

Second, mantras are usually practiced for a certain number of minutes; shabads are practiced for a certain number of repetitions. Shabads are usually practiced for 11 or 26 or 54 or 108 repetitions. It helps to use a *mala* or rosary to keep track of the repetitions. At the end of the final repetition, we repeat the last two lines twice. As with most other meditations, it is best to pick a shabad and practice it for 40 or 90 or 120 or 1000 or more days.

Shabads are useful if you have physical challenges that make it difficult to hold a position for any length of time or if you have environmental challenges that make it difficult to find a place to practice. This is because you can practice shabads without using any particular mudra or sitting position. I have seen people use shabads while walking, and I once had the opportunity to practice shabads when I was in the hospital recovering from food poisoning. You really can recite a shabad just about anywhere.

There is one other use for shabads. Spiritual practice at its best includes physical yoga for the body, meditation for the mind, and some sort of prayer or inspirational reading for the soul. You can certainly use prayers from your own tradition for this purpose. But if you are at a loss for what to do for the prayerful reading part of your practice, try the shabads. They work for everyone.

PRONUNCIATION GUIDE

The more accurately you pronounce the mantras and shabads, the greater the effect is on the consciousness. This pronounciation guide is a system for pronouncing Gurmukhi, the language of the mantras and shabads.

Vowels–Long vowels are held slightly longer than they are in English.

Long Vowels include:

aa as in father

ay as in say

ai as in mess

ee as in seen

oo as in soon

o as in so

aau as in cow or as in God

Short Vowels include:

a as in but

i as in win

u as in put

Notes: *Eh* at the end of a word is pronounced like it is in English. *Ek* rhymes with neck.

Accent–The accented syllable in a word is the first syllable with a long vowel. Where a word has only short vowels, the accent is on the first syllable.

Aspirated Consonants–Where an h immediately follows a consonant, we expel extra breath to create the sound. Note that th is pronounced as it is in Thailand.

Retroflexed Consonants–Retroflexed sounds are made by flipping the tongue to the upper palate where the hard palate meets the soft palate, allowing the tongue to flip forward to complete the sound. Retroflexed consonants are indicated by an underline.

Special Sounds–The "r" in Gurmukhi is made by touching the tongue to the upper palate just above the teeth. It will sound almost like a d. The sound ng is a nasal sound. In mantras, this nasal sound is accented.

POINTERS FOR PRACTICE

–Always tune in before practicing Kundalini Yoga and meditation. (See p. 2)

–Do Kundalini Yoga on an empty stomach, do not eat for at least two hours prior to doing yoga.

– Wear clothing suitable for exercise. Natural fiber clothing, preferably white, is best. A white cotton headcovering is advisable. Leave the feet bare.

–For your practice of Kundalini Yoga, pick a clean environment that is free from interruptions and distractions. A carpeted space is ideal. The temperature should be comfortable. Use a natural fiber blanket or an animal skin to sit on for insulation and padding.

–All breathing is done through the nose unless otherwise specified.

–To hold the breath, simply suspend your breathing. Keep your throat relaxed. Don't tighten up.

–Unless otherwise specified, a way to maintain a good meditative focus is by mentally chanting *Sat* on the inhale and *Naam* on the exhale. *Sat Naam* rhymes with "but mom." Sat means Truth; Naam means Name. This mantra helps us focus on our Truth.

–Drink plenty of water afterwards to re-hydrate yourself and flush toxins out of your system.

–Do your best, strive for excellence, but if you experience nausea, dizziness, or severe pain, STOP.

–Maintain the order of the exercises in the sets. You may cut down the times of the exercises in most cases, but do not leave exercises out. However, you may use some of the easier exercises as warm-ups before doing a regular set.

–Do not exceed the maximum times given with the exception of the relaxation times.

–Enjoy yourself! Keeping a smile on your face, unless otherwise specified, helps maintain a positive attitude and a positive experience.

–Unless otherwise specified, conclude an exercise or meditation by inhaling, holding the breath briefly while circulating the energy, then exhaling and relaxing the position. Inhale with the body centered.

–During meditation and meditative exercises, always keep the spine straight unless otherwise specified.

–Unless otherwise specified, always apply *Neck Lock* during meditation by tucking in the chin so that the neck is in line with the rest of the spine.

–Some sets and meditations specify particular musical tapes. Tapes and CDs may be purchased through the resources listed in the back of the book. In most cases, you may substitute other appropriate music or practice the exercise without accompaniment. 3HO music is preferred as its vibration enhances the practice of this form of yoga.

–It's a good idea to wrap yourself, especially the lower part of your torso, in a natural fiber shawl or blanket during meditation.

–It is natural to experience heat sometimes during meditation when the energy starts moving, so don't let this bother you.

–Women in the heaviest part of their period or past the first trimester of pregnancy should avoid Sat Kriya, Breath of Fire, heavy navel pumping exercises, Root Lock, Diaphragm Lock, Stretch Pose, and inverted poses, including Plow Pose.

–Kundalini Yoga and meditation are suitable for children, except for Sat Kriya, Root Lock, and Breath of Fire. These exercises may be practiced by children after puberty. Depending on the child's age, it will probably be necessary to cut down the times of the exercises.

Yoga for Prosperity

THE NUTS AND BOLTS OF PROSPERITY

*"Actually, being spiritual means that your spirit is your hub. I am.
I am. And you do not barter your dignity, integrity, personality.
Then once you achieve that, all the wealth comes to you."*

Yogi Bhajan

Anna was a bitter woman. She lost all her savings and investments during the Great Depression, and blamed her brother for her loss. Eventually, she extended her resentment to include her whole family. During the Depression, she scrimped and wore frayed clothes. She dined on freebies whenever possible. This pattern continued even after the Great Depression ended and she had more money.

She had no friends, never married and never even had a sweetheart. She was eventually estranged from everyone in her family with the exception of one niece she wasn't all that close to. By dint of investing and reinvesting whatever money she had, her estate was worth more than $20 million at the time of her death many years later. Although a multi-millionaire, she died with poverty consciousness, never enjoying the fruits of her efforts. But despite the bitterness and misery of her life, after she died, she gave that money to a university to provide scholarships for financially challenged young women; a noble

What is prosperity? Since this book contains many techniques for achieving prosperity, we should understand what prosperity is so we will recognize it when we receive it. This chapter is an overview of what prosperity is and isn't. The following two true stories serve to illustrate.

endeavor. But it's still debatable whether she lived to her destiny while she was alive.

In contrast, there was a family that lost all their savings and investments during the Depression. The father retained his job (albeit at a reduced salary); the family owned their house free and clear. The children were feeling no hardship, so they were surprised when the mother announced that she would be selling some of her heirloom furniture. Over a period of two to three years, the mother sold off a little used guest bed, some side chairs, a side table, some fancy glassware.....nothing the family really needed. Many years passed and the mother died. At the funeral, one of the daughters noticed that there were many more people present than she was expecting. An old classmate of her mother's introduced himself after the funeral. The daughter expressed gratitude and surprise that the man would take the time to show such respect for a woman he probably hadn't seen in decades. The man said, "In the Depression, your family had little, but mine had nothing. For three years, your mother fed us."

The woman in the second story was acting from a position of empowerment. She didn't wring her hands and say, "What a pity!" and then do nothing about her neighbors' plight. She empowered herself to find and act on a solution to her neighbors' destitution, and thereby empowered them as well. The woman in the first story displayed feelings of powerlessness. Even after she had a wealth of funds that could have been used in empowering ways, her fear and anger prevented her from achieving real prosperity during her lifetime.

PROSPERITY CONSCIOUSNESS

What makes us recognize true prosperity when we see it and distinguish it from poverty masquerading as prosperity? Here are some general statements about prosperity consciousness.

Chapter 2: The Nuts and Bolts of Prosperity

1. Prosperity is the opposite of neediness; prosperous people have their needs met, and the needs of those they care for are met also.
2. Prosperity is the opposite of greed; prosperous people allow the flow of money and goods through their lives.
3. Prosperous people do not hoard toxic emotions.
4. Prosperous people exhibit self-esteem and self-worth.
5. Prosperous people are empowered and empowering.
6. Prosperous people are open-hearted and open-handed.
7. Prosperity is a state in which prayers are answered.
8. Prosperous people have expansive mental parameters; they are intuitive and creative.
9. Prosperity is inspiring and elevating. It touches our hearts and souls.
10. Prosperous people fulfill their destinies, and they have whatever it takes to fulfill their destinies.

According to Yogi Bhajan, master of Kundalini Yoga: "A prosperous person has certain characteristics. For that person richness itself is not the basic aim. It happens anyway. A prosperous person does not gather wealth, but the wealth of wealths. No matter what the circumstances, a prosperous person creates, delivers, and fulfills. They act with a constant equilibrium through all pressures and all shortcomings. That person will not barter the values of their character or identity for any temporary benefit. They always remember the presence and possibilities of the Infinite within each person. They cultivate endurance, dedication, and awareness. To such a person, prosperity is as natural as the breath, as unlimited as the mind and as immediate as this moment."

Prosperity consciousness is a state of harmony between mind, body, and spirit. Despite our outer circumstances (rich or poor), when we live in a cozy manner, trusting the Universe to care for our needs, then we are truly wealthy.

Yoga for Prosperity

THE BREATH OF PROSPERITY: PRANAYAM

"One prosperous thought is more powerful than a thousand thoughts of failure." Yogi Bhajan

Yogi Bhajan says: "We want to leave with you certain knowledge which will serve you, your personality, your reality, your own self. You will become prosperous. You will say, "How?" The more prana the body consumes, the more wealth comes. It's a simple law. People with short breath are always absolutely poor. They 'half-breathe.' They breathe only in the upper area. So they do not touch the heavens and the earth "

This chapter explains how to perform basic yogic breathing techniques and why deep breathing is important to prosperity. Included are two breath meditations.

Think about it. The first gift you received when you emerged as a living, being from your mother's womb was the breath. Breathing deeply, you are fully accepting this first and foremost of all gifts, and thereby accepting the gift of life in all its richness. Breathing shallowly, you are denying the richness you could receive from life, automatically telling yourself, "There is not enough." Deep breathing is an important key to a rich and full life.

Prana is life force energy. The pranic body is the body of that life force energy. Pranayam is the science of controlling the prana through the breath. What is important for the experience of prosperity is that the pranic body controls the three mental bodies, the negative, positive, and neutral minds. When we breathe deeply, the pranic body is strong. This means that the mental bodies are strong as well. Control your breath, control your mind; control your mind, control your life.

For prosperity it is especially important that the positive mind be strong and balanced. It helps us to see the good in others and ourselves. We see opportunities, and feel worthy. This means we accept prosperity when it comes to us, and we don't self-destruct.

Deep breathing also contributes to the experience of fearlessness. This is important to the experience of prosperity, because when we are fearful, we freeze up and the flow of prosperity stops.

Deep breathing enhances health, strengthens both the immune system and the nervous system, helps relieve stress and tension, and enhances both intuition and the electromagnetic field. So the quality of our lives improves the more deeply we breathe. With deep breathing we have the energy, health, and inner strength to follow through on projects for our prosperous good.

BASIC BREATHING TECHNIQUES

Long Deep Breathing—Long deep breathing is both calming and energizing. It may be done any time, all the time, anywhere. Watch a child's abdomen rise and fall as he or she breathes, and you will understand how to do this simplest and most basic of breathing techniques. Allow your abdomen to expand as you inhale and contract as you exhale. The shoulders move little or not at all. Breathe as slowly and deeply as possible. Breathing is through the nose unless otherwise specified.

Left Nostril Breathing—Left nostril breathing is calming

and helps us become receptive. Block the right nostril with the right thumb and breathe exclusively through the left nostril. Left nostril breathing may be done as a separate exercise, usually for 3 minutes.

Right Nostril Breathing–Right nostril breathing is an energizing breath. Block the left nostril with the left thumb and breathe exclusively through the right nostril. Right nostril breathing may be done as a separate exercise, usually for 3 minutes.

Breath of Fire–This is a very energizing and purifying breath. Breath of Fire is basically long deep breathing speeded up to 2-3 breaths per second. It helps if you focus on the exhale, pulling in the navel and expelling air, and allow the inhale to happen as a matter of course, keeping a good rhythm with the inhale and exhale equal in length. Breath of Fire may be done as an exercise for 3 minutes or more after tuning in.

Sitali Pranayam - This is a cooling, healing breath that helps release anger. Inhale through the rolled tongue with the tip of the tongue just outside the lips. Exhale long and deep through the nose. If you are unable to roll your tongue, then inhale through the mouth with the tongue just past the lips. This may also be done as an exercise in its own right, breathing as slowly as possible for 3 minutes or more.

KUNDALINI YOGA AND MEDITATION FOR THE BREATH
ONE MINUTE BREATH MEDITATION

The practice of this meditation promotes health, increases energy, steadies the mind, enhances intuition, and connects us to the flow of spirit. For a greater prosperity focus, feel free to play one of the musical tapes mentioned in this book while you meditate. (See Resources)

Inhale slowly for 20 seconds or as long as is comfortable. Hold the breath for 20

21

seconds or as long as is comfortable. Exhale for 20 seconds or as long as is comfortable. There is no specific hand posture or eye focus. Keep the spine straight, in any comfortable sitting position. Continue for 11 minutes.

The goal here is to build up to the 20-second breath patterns. Almost no one is capable of doing this without diligent practice, but the goal is to increase each increment of time until you are breathing only once a minute. That is where the true treasure lies.

MEDITATION FOR FEARLESSNESS AND OPENNESS

Practicing this meditation allows us to be open to the flow of prosperity in our lives without fear. It stimulates the pituitary and enhances intuition.

The *Saa Taa Naa Maa* mantra is a sound current of regeneration. In Easy Pose with the spine straight, relax the upper arms by the sides hugging the torso. The forearms are parallel to the ground with the palms facing up and the hands in Closed Lotus Mudra with all the fingertips touching. Separate the hands about 3 feet from each other. Feel relaxed. Focus at the brow point with the eyes one-tenth open. Inhale deeply, then exhale completely. Hold the breath out and mentally chant Saa Taa Naa Maa 4 times, applying Root Lock by pulling in on the navel and up on the sex organ and anal sphincter muscle as the breath is held out. Keep the throat relaxed. Inhale and repeat. Continue for 11-31 minutes.

Wheels of Prosperity: the Chakras

"What happens when you become saintly and you talk to your soul? You become rich and prosperous." Yogi Bhajan

The chakras are vortices of energy, located along the spine, which correspond to our varied capabilities as human beings. We awaken, open, strengthen and balance the chakras by raising the kundalini which is a coil of energy that usually lies dormant at the base of the spine. This coil of energy, this kundalini, is specifically activated by all Kundalini Yoga and meditation, and also by practicing the shabads. When the kundalini energy is raised, we can access all our potentials and live wholesome, fully realized lives. A fully realized life includes both God-consciousness and prosperity.

This chapter is an overview of the **chakras** and how each of the eight chakras affects the experience of prosperity. The chapter includes a Kundalini Yoga set, suitable for beginners, that energizes all eight chakras, plus a beginner's meditation for opening the chakras and experiencing prosperity.

There are eight chakras. Each has different qualities, corresponding to a different point on our bodies.

First Chakra - The first chakra is located at the base of the spine near the rectum. It is associated with the sense of smell, the element of earth, and the color red. It is associated with our basic capacity for survival, our basic capacity to eliminate what is toxic from our lives, and our basic capacity to assimilate what will nourish us.

When the first chakra is weak or imbalanced, our most basic needs may not be met. We may eliminate from our lives what would nourish us and hoard what is toxic. Thus, both extreme poverty and extreme materialism are usually indications that the first chakra is out of balance.

When the first chakra is strong and balanced, we allow what we need into our lives. We have the grit to survive. We eliminate clutter and toxic situations from our lives.

A strong and balanced first chakra is essential for prosperity in its most elemental sense. Without it, we are needy and impoverished. With it, we have the foundation on which true prosperity can rest.

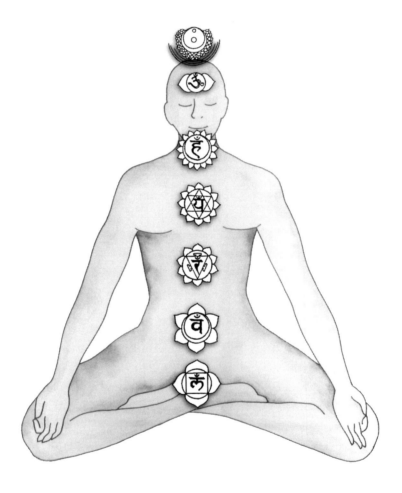

Second Chakra - The second chakra is located just above the first chakra in the area of the sex organs. It is associated with the sense of taste, the element of water, and the color orange. It is associated with the flow of life, our capacities for creativity and enjoyment, and our sexuality.

When the second chakra is weak or imbalanced, our lives are dull, flat, savorless, life-denying and rigid. Alternately, there can be problems with promiscuity or other forms of "tasteless" sexual expression to the exclusion of other forms of creativity.

When the second is strong and balanced, we are creative and have the capacity to enjoy life. We express our sexuality in positive, appropriate, life-affirming ways. There is a good flow to our lives.

A strong and balanced second chakra is essential to experience the flow of goods, joyful abundance, and prosperity in our lives. It provides the creativity and the enjoyment that make prosperity a real possibility. It is certainly possible to have loads of money without having an open and strong second chakra, but it isn't possible to enjoy it.

Third Chakra - The third chakra is located at the navel point where all the nerve endings meet. It is associated with the sense of sight, the element of fire, and the color yellow. It is associated with our capacity to set a goal and see it through, with empowerment, and with health and energy.

When the third chakra is weak or imbalanced, we tend to be plagued with anger, resentment, depression, and ill-health. It is difficult to set goals, follow a vision, and see things through. Alternately, if it is strong but imbalanced, we can be greedy, overbearing and ruthless towards our fellow humans in the pursuit of our goals.

When the third chakra is strong and balanced, we are energetic, enthusiastic and generally healthy. We feel empowered to follow our visions through to completion. We feel we "have what it takes." We use our drive to get where we need to go.

Empowered prosperity requires a strong and balanced third chakra. It provides both the vision and the willpower to make our dreams come true.

Lower Triangle - The first three chakras are known as the lower triangle. They form the foundation on which the other chakras rest.

Fourth Chakra - The fourth chakra is located at the heart center. It is associated with the sense of touch, the element of air, and the color green. It is associated with our capacities for love, compassion, patience, gratitude and generosity.

When the fourth chakra is weak or imbalanced, hatred and jealousy may be a problem. We may be "green with envy." We may tend to be on the take and never on the give except for self-serving reasons. Or we may be lonely intellectuals, stuck in the head, and denying the heart. Alternately, we may be "smother lovers," people whose love is a possessive, stifling caricature of the real thing, notably lacking in space and air. In any of these scenarios, fear will rule us.

When the fourth chakra is strong and balanced, we are loving, kind, compassionate, patient, grateful, and generous with ourselves and our goods. Our love will have the space and air in it to allow others to be what they need to be. We will touch the hearts and lives of others in ways that buoy them up.

The green energy of the heart is important to the green energy of prosperity. Life is rich and full when we experience real love and gratitude. Generosity makes us feel wealthy, and opens the flow of prosperity into our lives. Without an open heart, any semblance of prosperity we experience will feel like a sham.

Fifth Chakra - The fifth chakra is located at the throat. It is associated with the sense of hearing, the element of ether, and the color blue. It is associated with our human capacities for communication and truth.

When the fifth chakra is weak or imbalanced, we may have a problem speaking up for ourselves or others. Communication is difficult. Alternately, we may speak the truth so bluntly that no one wants to hear it or even be in the same century with us.

When the fifth chakra is strong and balanced, we communicate our truth easily and powerfully. Others clearly hear and understand what we have to say. Our prayers are likely to be answered.

If we want our prayers for prosperity to be answered, a strong and balanced fifth chakra is a big asset. Similarly, it is a big asset for all the communicating we must do to prosper.

Sixth Chakra - The sixth chakra is located at the brow point, centered between the eyes and just a bit above them in front of the pituitary. It is associated with the color indigo. It is associated with wisdom, insight, intuition, and the "sixth sense."

When the sixth chakra is weak or imbalanced, we will be plagued with doubt, confusion, and worry. We will tend to make poor choices and to be at the wrong place at the wrong time.

When the sixth chakra is strong and balanced, we will be insightful, intuitive, and experience strong inner knowing. We will generally be at the right place at the right time, and our choices will tend to be excellent.

Knowledge can be our greatest wealth. Making wise choices and being at the right place at the right time help make prosperity a reality. Thus a strong and balanced sixth chakra can be a most important tool for the experience of prosperity.

Seventh Chakra - The seventh chakra is located at the crown of the head. It is associated with the pineal gland, and the color violet. The seventh chakra is sometimes called the "seat of the soul." It is associated with our capacities for vastness, boundlessness, universality, humility, and oneness of spirit with the Infinite and all creation.

When the seventh chakra is weak or imbalanced, we tend to be egotistical. We live in a limited vision of reality and tend to be disconnected from our Source. Our soul connection tends to be weak.

When the seventh chakra is strong and balanced, we are very connected to our Source. We experience vast inner richness and hear the call of the soul easily. This is prosperity in its most divine sense, this vast sense of unlimited richness and this total connection to the Source of all things.

Higher Triangle - Chakras five, six, and seven are known as the higher triangle. When the kundalini energy is flowing freely, excess lower chakra energy moves up to these centers so that our awareness expands and our hidden talents emerge.

Eighth Chakra - The eighth chakra is the *aura*, which is the body's electro-magnetic field. As the transpersonal chakra, it is not associated with any point on our physical bodies. It extends out from our physical bodies in all directions, including up and down, forming a protective field. It is associated with the qualities of radiance and magnetism. The openness, strength, and balance of all the other chakras will show up in the aura.

When the aura is weak or imbalanced, we have little defense against outside negativity. We are rarely ourselves, either taking on whatever is in the environment or being a drain on others. Either way, we will not be magnetic or inspiring people.

A strong and balanced aura acts like a philosopher's stone, because it transmutes outside negativity into something positive or neutral. When the aura is strong and balanced, we are magnetic, inspiring, and radiant. We elevate and reach out to others by our mere presence.

A strong and balanced aura is necessary for our prosperity to be truly inspirational and to allow what we need to reach us. We will not feel buffeted by "the slings and arrows of outrageous fortune." We will prosper instead.

To fully manifest our destinies, to live divinely rich and full lives, to awaken all our dormant potentials, to experience prosperity in its fullest sense requires that all the chakras be open, strong and balanced. The following Kundalini Yoga sets and meditations are excellent tools for opening and balancing all of the chakras.

KUNDALINI YOGA AND MEDITATION FOR THE CHAKRAS
BASIC SPINAL ENERGY SET

This is an easy set, excellent for beginners. In fact, it may be used as a warm-up, although it is usually practiced on its own prior to meditation. This set energizes all the chakras, improves spinal flexibility, and enhances the flow of spinal fluid to the brain, which in turn enhances mental alertness.

1. Spinal Flexes: Sitting in Easy Pose, grab the ankles with both hands. Inhale and stretch the spine forward so that the chest lifts up. Exhale and stretch the spine backwards. The head should stay level without flopping up and down. Gradually increase the pace as the spine warms up. Continue for 26-108 repetitions. Inhale. Relax for 1 minute.

2. Spinal Flexes in Rock Pose: Sitting on the heels, place the hands palms down on the thighs. Again stretch the spine forward on the inhale, and stretch it backwards on the exhale. Think Sat on the inhale and Naam on the exhale. Continue for 26-108 repetitions.Inhale. Relax for 2 minutes.

3. Spinal Twists: Sitting in Easy Pose, bring the hands to the shoulders with the fingers in front and the thumbs in back. Inhale and twist to the left. Exhale and twist to the right. Breathe long and deep. Continue for 26 repetitions. Inhale facing forward. Relax for 1 minute.

4. Bear Grip See-saw: Sitting in Easy Pose, lock the fingers in bear grip by hooking the fingers together with the left palm facing out and the right palm facing the chest. Keeping the locked finger in front of the heart center, move the elbows up and down like a see-saw.

29

Breathe long and deep with the motion. Continue for 26 repetitions.Inhale straight, then exhale and pull on the lock. Relax for 30 seconds.

5. Upper Spinal Flexes: Sitting in Easy Pose, hold the knees firmly with the hands. Keeping the elbows straight, inhale and stretch the upper spine forward. Exhale and stretch the upper spine backwards. Continue for 26-108 repetitions.Inhale. Relax for 1 minute.

6. Shoulder Shrugs: Sitting in Easy Pose with the hands on the knees, inhale and pull both shoulders up. Exhale and relax them down. Continue for 2 minutes. Inhale, pull the shoulders up, and hold the breath for 15 seconds. Exhale and relax the shoulders.

7. Neck rolls: Sitting in Easy Pose with the hands on the knees, carefully and gently roll the neck in a clockwise direction 5 times. Then reverse the direction and roll the neck counter-clockwise 5 times. Inhale with the head straight and then exhale.

8. Sitting in Easy Pose, hook the fingers together in Bear Grip at the throat level. Inhale and apply root lock, pulling up on the anal sphincter muscle and sex organ while pulling in on the navel. Exhale and apply Root Lock. Then raise the hands above the head while maintaining the Bear Grip. And again inhale and apply Root Lock, and exhale and apply Root Lock. Repeat this cycle 2 more times for a total of 3 times.

9. Sat Kriya: Sitting on the heels, stretch the arms overhead with the arms hugging the ears. Interlace the fingers except for the index fingers which point straight up. Focus at the brow point. Chant *Sat* and pull in on the navel, then chant *Naam* and release it. Continue for 3 minutes. Then inhale and squeeze the energy all the way from the base of the spine to the top of the head.

Note: Sat Kriya may be done separately for 3-31 minutes, preferably after warming-up, as an exercise *kriya* in its own right. Always rest on the back for at least the same amount of time as you do Sat Kriya, and preferably for twice the amount of time. It is not a recommended practice for pre-pubescent children, women past the first trimester of pregnancy, or women who are menstruating.

10. Corpse Pose: Deeply relax on the back with the arms by the sides, palms up and the legs straight. Continue for 15 minutes.

A Beginners' Mantra Meditation for the Chakras

The practice of this mantra paves the way for the effectiveness of other mantras. It is thus an excellent practice for beginners. In addition to opening all the chakras, it also promotes prosperity, creativity, opportunity, and protection.

This mantra is a subtle weaving of sound which may be translated, "That Infinite Totality is here, everywhere. That creativity of God is here, everywhere." Remember to pull in the navel slightly when chanting *Har*, and to touch the tongue to the upper palate just above the teeth for all the "r" sounds. The "ng" is a slightly extended nasal sound. Remember also that "Rang" is pronounced like the English word "Rung."

Sit in any meditative position with the spine straight. With the arms straight and resting over the knees, touch the tip of the thumb to

31

the tip of the little finger (Buddhi Mudra) with the other fingers straight and relaxed. Become very calm. Listen silently to the mantra *Saa Ray Saa Saa, Saa Ray Saa Saa, Saa Ray Saa Saa Saa Rang, Har Ray Har Har, Har Ray Har Har, Har Ray Har Har Har Rang* either with the tape (see Resources) or in your mind for 1 minute. Feel the dance of it in all your cells. Then chant the mantra out loud for 11-31 minutes. This meditation was origianlly taught using the tape Sa Re Sa Sa by Guru Shabad Singh Khalsa.

THE TEN BODIES OF PROSPERITY

"To enjoy prosperity and self-fulfillment, maintain your purity from the time you open your eyes until the time you close your eyes." Yogi Bhajan

In addition to the chakras, we also are blessed with ten bodies: the Soul Body, the Negative Mind, the Positive Mind, the Neutral Mind, the Physical Body, the Arcline, the Aura, the Pranic Body, the Subtle Body and the Radiant Body. These bodies serve as archetypes or facets of our wholeness, which correspond to the many capacities we have as human beings. Prosperity and joy are some of the gifts of ten strong and balanced yogic bodies.

The Soul Body - This is our starting point and our ending point. Without the soul body, we would not exist. It is our microcosm of the Infinite, our creative spark and the key to our destinies.

This chapter explains the concept of the ten yogic bodies and how they affect prosperity. You will find a basic Kundalini Yoga set for awakening the ten bodies and an explanation of how to chant Mool Mantra, **the mantra of choice** for strengthening the ten bodies, plus a special meditation.

When the soul body is strong, we are creative, humbly alive to the Infinite Creative Power within us. We follow the call of our destinies. We live from our hearts in balance with our intuition.

When the soul body is weak, we tend to be stuck, bottled up, rigid, and egocentric. We tend to follow parental and cultural "shoulds" rather than the call of the soul. We get caught in the limitations of intellectual games.

From the viewpoint of prosperity, a strong soul body grants us the humility to use what we have creatively, to allow the flow of goods and spirit in our lives. We relate to Infinity, so the Infinite provides us with everything.

The Negative Mind - The negative mind is not negative. It is that part of our minds which assesses the dangers inherent in any given situation. It is that part of us which is obedient and longs to belong, just as we were obedient out of a longing for their love when our parents told us not to do something.

When the negative mind is strong and balanced, we assess the dangers inherent in a situation accurately. We obey the call of our higher consciousness, or at least of our conscience. We channel our longing to belong in appropriate ways.

When the negative mind is weak, we will do all sorts of unwise things to fit in, to be liked, to belong. We will obey everything except our own good sense. Conversely, if the negative mind is unbalanced and too strong, we may see dangers where none exist.

From the viewpoint of prosperity, the negative mind must be strong and balanced, or we're either going to fritter away our time and resources on scams and deadbeat "friends" or we're going to be too fearful to act on those wonderful opportunities life has to offer us. When it is strong and balanced, we can say "no" when needed, to obey the call of destiny.

The Positive Mind - The positive mind assesses the benefits, the opportunities, and the positive good inherent in any situation or person.

When the positive mind is strong and balanced, we see the good in ourselves and therefore experience self worth. We see the good in everyone and therefore treat all people in an even-handed way. We see opportunities as they arise. No matter what is happening we will see "the silver lining." We face life with confidence and good humor.

When the positive mind is weak, we are cursed with guilt, anger, resentment and other forms of negativity. We don't like ourselves, and we don't like anyone else either. We don't see much good in anything.

Conversely, if the positive mind is too strong and unbalanced, we may be so happy-go-lucky that we mess ourselves up. We may be blithely unaware that anything might be wrong. We may go for the gusto when it is not to our benefit or anyone else's to do so. Or we may be greedy and grabby, making everyone around us miserable.

A strong and balanced positive mind is almost the definition of prosperity because it brings self worth, a freedom from negativity, and the ability to spot opportunities and the "silver lining."

The Neutral Mind - Once we have assessed the dangers and benefits inherent in a situation, it is the job of the neutral mind to make a decision.

When the neutral mind is strong, we make wise decisions easily and quickly. We act in a spirit of service for the greater good. Our minds have a meditative purity and peace, free of prejudice.

When the neutral mind is weak, we tend to be painfully indecisive. Conversely, we may make snap decisions based on prejudices and bigotry. Service will not be our strong suit. The mind will not be at peace.

Wise decisions lead to prosperity. As we serve, so does the Universe serve us. So the peace of a strong, balanced neutral mind brings the blessings of prosperity to us and all around us.

The Physical Body - This is the body we most often relate to. It is the vehicle for carrying around the other bodies. It is the balance point between our inner and outer realities.

When the physical body is strong, we are balanced beings. We have the strength to make whatever sacrifices are necessary to carry through the decisions of the neutral mind. We have the ability to be living examples and teachers.

When the physical body is weak, our inner and outer realities will tend to be out of balance. Our lives will tend to be out of balance, and we will be lazy and self-indulgent. We will not make the sacrifices necessary to carry through the decisions of the neutral mind. We will shy away from any situation where we need to be an example.

A strong physical body is necessary to take our prosperous ideas out of the realm of imagination and into the realm of manifestation.

The Arcline - The arcline is our "halo". Men and women both have an arcline which extends from ear to ear over the head. Women have a second arcline which extends from nipple to nipple across the heart. The halo, the arcline, acts like a radar device that both sends and receives information.

When the arcline is strong, we have the capacity to focus strongly. We can focus our words, and our words will be powerful and effective. We can focus our attention and intuitively know what is what. We will be at the right place at the right time doing the right thing.

When the arcline is weak, we tend to be scattered. Our words have little power. People who say, "No one listens to me," are actually saying, "I have a weak arcline." We will tend to be at the wrong place at the wrong time doing the wrong thing.

With a strong arcline, our prayers will be answered--a key factor for prosperity. Knowing what is what, and being at the right place at the right time are also vitally important for prosperity to manifest.

The Aura - All the qualities of the aura (eighth chakra) that were discussed in the chapter on the chakras apply here. In addition, it should be noted that when the aura is strong, we feel secure and nurtured. From that place of security, we are able to nurture others with kindness, compassion, and mercy. We will not only prosper, but everyone around us will prosper because of us.

The Pranic Body - The pranic body is our reservoir of life-force energy. It is carried on the breath. When it breaks, we die. The pranic body controls the three mental bodies, the negative, positive and neutral minds.

When the pranic body is strong, we have abundant energy. We are fearless, and generally healthy. Our mental bodies will be strong and balanced. Abundance is the gift of a strong pranic body.

When the pranic body is weak, we are fearful and depressed. We experience a scarcity of energy, a scarcity of health, a scarcity of joy, a scarcity of life. Scarcity and being scared result from a weak pranic body.

The Subtle Body - The subtle body is the only body besides the soul to survive physical death. It acts as the soul's record keeper. As it masters the subtle details of the soul's existence, so too it masters all the subtle details of our lives.

When the subtle body is strong, we experience mastery and the calm grasp of detail that is the hallmark of a master. Our lives exhibit subtlety, calmness, grace, and staying power.

When the subtle body is weak, we tend to be mystified. We fly off the handle quickly. Our lives have a gross and graceless quality.

Mastery attracts wealth and prosperity. So do grace and staying power. By contrast, flying off the handle, graceless action, and acting clueless all repel wealth and prosperity. So a strong subtle body leads with time and patience to strong prosperity.

The Radiant Body - The radiant body is the extra sparkle of the soul. It is our radiant light that extends beyond the aura to Infinity.

When the radiant body is strong, we are courageous, successful, and victorious in all circumstances, no matter what the obstacles. We always excel. Our purposes are fulfilled across all barriers of time and space, even after our physical deaths. People describe us as radiant. We are transparent vessels for the light of our souls. Thus a strong radiant body leads to successful prosperity.

When the radiant body is weak, we feel defeated and discouraged at every turn. We feel unfulfilled. We lack courage and wimp out quickly. Our light fails to shine.

The stronger all our ten bodies are, the more likely we are to experience soul-satisfying prosperity. Here are some tools for developing the prosperity that stems from ten strong bodies.

KUNDALINI YOGA & MEDITATION FOR THE TEN BODIES

SET TO AWAKEN YOUR TEN BODIES

Practicing this set stimulates and strengthens all ten Bodies. It is also a good practice for enhancing flexibilty and strengthening the nervous system.

The Laya Yoga meditation that ends this set balances all the chakras and elevates the spirit. The words literally mean "One Creator Creation, Truth Name, Infinitely Great Wow! Indescribable Ecstasy Wisdom." It may be practiced on its own for 11-31 minutes.

1. Stretch Pose: Lying on the back with the arms by the sides, point the toes and raise the head and legs 6 inches off the ground. Bring the arms up so that the fingers point toward the toes. Focus the eyes on the tips of the toes. Do Breath of Fire. Continue for 1-3 minutes.

2. Lying on the back, bring the knees to the chest with the arms wrapped around the knees. Bring the nose between the knees or as close as possible. Hold this position with Breath of Fire. Continue for 1-3 minutes.

3. Sitting in Easy Pose or sitting between the heels in *Celibate Pose*, raise the arms up to a 60° angle with the fingertips touching the mounds just below the fingers. The thumbs point up, and the rest of the fingers are parallel to the ground. Close the eyes, focus at the brow point, and do Breath of Fire. Continue for 1-3 minutes.

38

4. Sitting with the legs spread wide on the ground, inhale with the arms overhead and exhale bringing the hands down to alternate toes (or whatever you can reach) starting with the left side. Continue 1-3 minutes.

5. With the legs still spread wide on the ground, hold onto the toes (or whatever you can reach). Inhale and bow straight down to the ground or as far as you can go. Exhale and sit back up. Continue for 1-3 minutes.

6. Spinal Flexes: Sitting in Easy Pose, grab the shins with the hands. Inhale and flex the spine forward, rocking forward on the buttocks. Exhale and flex the spine backwards, rolling backwards on the buttocks. Keep the head fairly level and the arms as straight and relaxed as you can. Continue for 1-3 minutes.

7. Sit on the heels with the hands flat on the thighs. Inhale and flex the spine forward. Exhale and flex the spine back. Focus at the brow point. Continue for 1-3 minutes.

8. Sitting on the heels, grasp the shoulders with the fingers in front and the thumb in back. Inhale and twist to the left. Exhale and twist to the right. Keep the arms parallel to the ground. Continue 1-3 minutes.

9. Sitting on the heels, place the hands on the shoulders as in the previous exercise. Inhale and raise the elbows up so that the backs of the wrists touch behind the neck. Exhale and return to the starting position. Continue for 1-3 minutes.

10. Sitting on the heels, interlace the fingers in Venus Lock. Inhale and raise the arms over the head. Exhale and bring the hands down to the lap. Keep the arms fairly straight. Continue for 1-3 minutes.

11. Sitting in Easy Pose with the hands on the knees, inhale and shrug the left shoulder up. Exhale and raise the right shoulder while lowering the left shoulder. Continue for 1 minute. Reverse the direction, inhaling and raising the right shoulder, then exhaling while raising the left shoulder and lowering the right shoulder. Continue for 1 minute.

12. Sitting in Easy Pose with the hands on the knees, inhale and shrug both shoulders up. Exhale and lower them. Continue for 1 minute.

13. Sitting in Easy Pose with the hands on the knees, inhale and turn the head to the left. Exhale and turn the head to the right. Continue for 1 minute. Reverse the direction, inhaling and turning the head to the right, exhaling and turning the head to the left. Continue for 1 minute.

14. Frog Pose: Squat down with the buttocks on or near the heels, with the heels touching each other off the ground. The fingertips are on the ground between the knees. The head is up. Inhale powerfully, straighten the legs and raise the buttocks, leaving the fingertips on the ground and allowing the head to come down, leaving the heels if possible off the ground. Exhale powerfully and return to the position. Continue for 26-54 repetitions.

15. Relax completely on the back in corpse pose for 5 minutes or more.

16. Laya Yoga Meditation: Sitting cross-legged with the hands in *Gyan Mudra*, chant Ek Ong Kaar-a, Sat-a Naam-a, Siri Waa-a, Hay Guroo. Apply Root Lock by pulling in on the navel and up on the anal sphincter muscle and sex organ as you chant the final - "*a*" sounds. Spin the chant mentally in three and a half circles starting at the base of the spine and going up to the top of the head. Continue for 11-31 minutes.

MOOL MANTRA

Chanting the *Mool Mantra* (also written Mul Mantra) aligns us with our souls and awakens our destinies. When I first learned about the ten bodies at a workshop given by Guruchander Singh Khalsa, DC, he stated that Mool Mantra is the mantra of choice for balancing all ten bodies. It contains everything. Chanting Mool Mantra raises the Kundalini, awakening all the charkas. *Mool* means root, and this mantra contains the foundation for all other mantras.

Mool Mantra may be sung or chanted in any melody for as long as you like. (A number of tapes and CDs available through the resources listed in the back of the book contain this mantra, including all the sadhana tapes and CDs.

Ek Ong Kaar—One Creator/Creation
Sat Naam—Truth Name
Kartaa Purkh—Doer Being (Active Principle of Creation)
Nirbhao—Without Fear
Nirvair—Without Revenge
Akaal Moorat—Undying Image
Ajooni—Unborn
Saibang—By Itself
Gurprasaad—Guru's Gift
Jap—Meditate! (or Recite!)
Aad Sach—In the beginning True

Jugaad Sach–Through the ages True
Haibee Sach–Even Now True
Naanak Hosee Bhee Sach–Nanak, It shall ever be True.
Emphasize the ch sounds as you chant.

SAHAJ SUKH DHIAAN

This is a silent Mool Mantra meditation on the breath. *Sahaj* refers to effortless flow and ease, an easy path to happiness and bliss. *Sukh* means comfort or peace. *Dhiaan* is deep meditation. This is a deep meditation for achieving inner peace and happiness and is an ancient technology. It combines all the benefits of deep breathing with all the benefits of chanting Mool Mantra. Practicing this meditation brings a lovely creative quality to the mind.

Keeping the chest lifted and the spine straight, sit in Easy Pose with the chin tucked slightly in, in Neck Lock. Eyes are closed. Inhale while silently chanting Mool Mantra twice. Feel the breath move up to the eyebrows and the root of the nose. Hold the breath and apply Diaphragm Lock by pulling in and up on the diaphragm while silently chanting Mool Mantra once. Then exhale while silently chanting Mool Mantra twice. No mudra is given. 108 complete breaths are said to redeem 8.4 million lifetimes. But start with 3-11 complete breaths. It helps to use a mala or rosary for this counting.

As an easier variation, you may inhale while silently chanting Mool Mantra once, hold the breath while applying Diaphragm Lock and silently chanting Mool Mantra 3 times, and exhale while silently chanting Mool Mantra once. In both cases, there are 5 repetitions of Mool Mantra per breath.

Self-Worth and Affirmative Action

"Make no excuses for your desire to be prosperous; it is a divine desire that should be given divine expression." Yogi Bhajan

A student once told me that his father had become very successful very quickly in his career, but had taken to drink and ended up destroying both his career and his marriage. Many of us know people like this. It's a common problem that stems from a lack of self-worth.

It takes self-respect to avoid destroying our character. It takes self-respect to avoid wallowing in guilt, anger, resentment, and other forms of negativity. And it takes self-respect to allow prosperity into our lives. People who become wealthy and superficially successful without a real sense of self-worth either end up destroying everything they have achieved, or they become miserable and miserly. Often, people with low self-worth prevent themselves from achieving any success, superficial or otherwise, due to their self-destructive habits or inner destitution.

Our self-esteem increases when we say "no" to self-destructive activities. It increases when we let go of

In this chapter, we look at the role self worth, self-affirmation, empowerment, and releasing negativity play in prosperity, including ways to change self-negating speech patterns and ways to use affirmations. Included are a Kundalini Yoga set for empowerment, two meditations for releasing negativity, a meditation for releasing excessive desire, two meditations for self-affirmation, plus a shabad for prosperity and releasing insecurity.

the negativity in our minds. Acknowledging that we deserve better can be an important first step towards self-worth and the blossoming of prosperity in our lives.

Nature abhors a vacuum. Once we let go of the negative, we are free to see the positive in ourselves, in others, and in the situations we are in, and we will notice positive opportunities as they arise. With the negative tension gone, we can relax and open up and receive the blessings life has in store for us.

With a positive attitude comes empowerment and the ability to act on opportunities as they arise. As we see the richness that is always there, we have more enthusiasm. As we acknowledge our goodness and worth, our actions become more effective. This creates a "win-win" cycle.

There are many ways of increasing self-worth and letting go of negativity. One of the most common is simply to change our thought and speech patterns. Instead of saying, "I don't have the money," we can say, "I have other priorities right now." Instead of saying, "I did a lousy job," we can say, "I'll get better as I get more practice." Making simple, positive changes to our casual speech patterns can make a world of difference.

It is also effective to speak or silently think affirmations. This type of affirmative action is not dishonest. Instead, it acknowledges that we are masterpieces created by the Master. We have no real right to belittle ourselves into misery, and every right to acknowledge our greatness as creations of the Creator.

Yogi Bhajan said: "You can make your world prosperous and happy by being you. There is never anything wrong with you because God made you, and God cannot be wrong."

You could say this whole book is about self-worth because every positive action we take increases our self-respect. Here are some particularly good practices for releasing negativity and increasing self-worth.

AFFIRMATIONS

Yogi Bhajan says, "Negative thoughts are the base of your misfortune and poverty—when you allow them, the loss is yours. Positive thoughts are the base of prosperity and contentment—when you allow them, the gain is yours."

This is the basis of affirmations. We become what we focus on. When we repeat positive thoughts and speak positive words, we can change a negative situation into a positive one.

SOME AFFIRMATIONS FOR PROSPERITY INCLUDE:

I deserve to prosper.

My life is rich and full.

I have everything I need to fulfill my destiny.

I have what it takes.

I am worthy, wealthy and wonderful.

I am healthy, wealthy and wise.

I am blessed with peace and prosperity.

I am showered with blessings.

Use your creativity to come up with other affirmations to suit your situation. It's best to frame your affirmation in a positive way, i.e. *"I have plenty of money"* is better than *"I don't have problems with money."* In addition, you may use the English translations of many of the shabads as affirmations.

Affirmations may be spoken out loud or repeated as a silent inner mantra. My personal experience is that using affirmations as a silent inner mantra works best, provided daily conversation reflects a positive attitude. But do try them both ways.

HERE ARE A FEW OF YOGI BHAJAN'S AFFIRMATIONS:

I am the Light of my Soul. I am beautiful. I am bountiful. I am bliss. I am. I am.

Healthy am I. Happy am I. Holy am I.

I am in success with my divine.

KUNDALINI YOGA & MEDITATION FOR SELF-WORTH AND RELEASING NEGATIVITY
SET FOR THE NAVEL CENTER

The practice of this set strengthens the navel chakra and enhances the sense of empowerment. It is good for digestion and helps eliminate gastric trouble. Like all navel center sets, it can help release anger.

(Note: The *Aap Sahaee Hoaa* mantra in Exercise 6 is a mantra for protection and prosperity. It may be translated, "The Lord Himself has become our Protector. The Truest of the True has taken care of us. God, God, God." The shabad, or spiritual poem, this mantra is derived from is given in its entirety in the Radiant Body Chapter. Many music tapes with this mantra are available through the resources listed in the back of this book.)

1. Sitting in Easy Pose with a straight spine, rest the upper arms against the ribcage and bend the elbows so that the forearms are parallel to the ground. With the palms well separated and facing each other, touch the thumb tips together. Open and close the fingers of both hands at the same time. Concentrate and move the fingers only. Continue for 4 minutes.

2. Lying on the back, place the fingers on the navel, keep the head relaxed on the ground and raise the heels up 6 inches. Press hard on the navel with both hands and raise the heels up to 18 inches. Then relax the pressure on the navel and lower the heels back down to 6 inches off the ground. Continue for 3 minutes. Proceed directly to the next exercise.

3. Lying on the back with the fingers on the navel and the heels 6 inches off the ground, press hard on the navel and raise the heels up to 80° (not quite straight up). Then relax the pressure on the navel and lower the heels back to 6 inches off the ground. Continue for 2 minutes.

4. Lying on the back, cup the hands under the buttocks. Raise the legs together up to 90°, spread the legs apart, then bring the legs back to together and lower them back to the ground. Continue this 4-part motion for 3 minutes.

5. Lying on the back, place the hands under the neck (not the head). Keeping the legs straight, alternately raise each leg to 90° and lower it back to the ground. Continue for 1 minute.

6. Lying on the back, lift both legs up to 90°, keeping the legs straight and the heels together. Hold the toes or whatever you can reach with both hands. Maintain the position and chant *Aap Sahaa-ee Hoaa Sachay Daa Sachaa Dhoaa, Har Har Har.* Continue for 7 minutes.

Then inhale, hold the breath for 15 seconds and bring the legs over the head into Plow Pose. The head and upper back are on the ground, and the hands remain on the toes. Exhale and relax down on your back.

7. Sitting with the legs spread as far apart as possible, grab the toes or whatever you can reach. Stretch the torso down towards the ground. Stretch down further gradually and gently for 8 counts, then raise the torso back up for 1 count. Continue this rhythm for 1 minute.

MEDITATION TO CONQUER SELF-ANIMOSITY

Practicing this meditation helps break the cycle of self-loathing and self-destructive activity. It enhances the qualities of constancy and steadiness and enables us to stay aligned with our core Truth. My personal experience is that practicing this meditation brings a joyful quality to the mind.

Sitting in Easy Pose with a straight spine, relax the arms by the sides and bring the hands up to the level of the heart. Make fists of the hands with the thumbs extended and pointing up. The fists and thumbs touch each other. Focus on the tip of the nose. Maintain an alert attitude and keep the torso steady (no rocking back and forth). Breathe in the following pattern: inhale deeply through the nose, exhale completely through the mouth. Inhale deeply and smoothly through the mouth, exhale completely through the nose. Continue for 3-11 minutes. (The time may be built up to 22 minutes, but no more.)

MEDITATION TO ELIMINATE NEGATIVE THOUGHTS

This is a good meditation to practice when you are plagued with persistent negative thoughts that prevent you from prospering or that are disrupting your life in any way. This particular meditation is best practiced only when you have thoughts that bother you; it isn't recommended to do long term.

Sitting in Easy Pose with a straight spine, make a cup of the hands with the right hand on top of the left and the fingers crossing each other. Relax the upper arms by the sides and place this mudra at the level of the heart. Look only into the cup. Meditate on the thought you don't like. Inhale deeply through the nose. Exhale completely in a long, dry, spitting motion through the puckered lips. Spit that awful thought out. Continue for 11 minutes. Then inhale and exhale. Maintain the mudra, close the eyes, breathe through the nose, and focus on the spine. Slowly draw the energy down the spine from the top to the bottom. Feel all 26 vertebrae. The more you feel the entire spine, the more relief you will feel.

BEGGAR'S MEDITATION

This meditation is designed for those times when you want something so badly you are making it impossible to manifest. It can be any kind of desire from the sublime to the ridiculous. Practicing this meditation calms the desire so it can manifest. I know people who have used this meditation successfully for prosperity. Note that although this meditation is similar to the last one, there are some differences. This meditation is also best as an occasional practice, not as a long-term one.

Sitting in Easy Pose with a straight spine, make a cup of the hands with the right hand on top of the left and the fingers crossing each other. Relax the upper arms by the sides and place this mudra at the level of the heart. Look only into the cup. Meditate on a single, strong desire. Inhale through the nose. Exhale completely in a long, dry spitting motion through the puckered lips. Spit the desire into the cup. Continue for 11 minutes.

MEDITATION FOR SELF-AFFIRMATION

Practicing this meditation powerfully affirms our purity, grace, and mastery, and thereby affirms our worthiness to receive. This is an affirmation to hold in consciousness as a guideline for our lives.

Sitting in Easy Pose with a straight spine, interlace the hands in Venus Lock in front of the heart center with the elbows relaxed down. Close the eyes. Chant in a monotone: *Me Within Me Is the Purity. Me Within Me Is the Reality. Me Within Me Is the Grace. I Am the Master of the Space.* Listen carefully as you chant. Continue for 11 minutes.

Then inhale deeply, hold the breath and tighten every fiber of the body in alignment with that purity. Then exhale. Repeat once more. Then inhale deeply, exhale, and relax.

THREE MINUTE MEDITATION FOR PROSPERITY AND SELF-ESTEEM

This is a short, sweet, and easy meditation. It may be done several times a day.

Sitting in Easy Pose with a straight spine, look down towards the center of the chin with closed eyes, or focus on the tip of the nose with the eyes one-tenth open. No mudra was specified for this meditation. Inhale deeply, hold the breath and mentally recite: *I am bountiful. I am blissful. I am beautiful.* Then exhale completely, hold the breath out and mentally recite: *Excel, excel, fearless.* Continue for 3 minutes.

SHABAD YOGA: JAA TOO MAYRAI VAL HAI FOR PROSPERITY AND RELEASING INSECURITY

This shabad is one of my favorites. Practicing it alleviates fears and insecurity as well as creating the experience of prosperity.

Jaa too mayrai val hai, taa ki-aa muhchhandaa.

Tudh sabh kichh maino, saapi-aa jaa tayraa bandaa.

Lakhamee tot na aava-ee, khaa-i kharach rahandaa.

Lakh chauraaseeh maydanee, sabh sayv karandaa.

Ayh vairee mitr sabh keeti-aa, neh mangeh maandaa.

Laykaa ko-i na puchha-ee, jaa har bakhshandaa.

Anand bha-i-aa sukh paa-i-aa, mil gur govindaa.

Sabhay kaaj savaari-ai, jaa tudh bhaavandaa.

Translation:

With You on my side, O Lord, what do I owe to any other?

You entrusted everything to me when I became Your slave.

My wealth is inexhaustible no matter how much I spend and consume.

8.4 million species all perform service unto me.

The enemies have all been made friends, and no one wishes me ill.

No one calls me to account as God is my Forgiver.

Bliss has welled up, and I have found peace meeting with the Guru-God.

Everything is perfectly arranged when You are pleased with me, O Lord.

Guru Arjan Dev. Pauri from Var of Rag Maroo Dakhanay. Siri Guru Granth Sahib, p.1096.

GREEN ENERGY AND THE HEART CHAKRA

"Those who want to be prosperous have to learn to make others prosperous. If you cannot make others prosperous, you cannot be prosperous...doesn't matter what you try." Yogi Bhajan

Has anyone ever felt poor while feeling full of love, gazing into the eyes of their beloved? Not likely. It's no coincidence that green, the color associated with the heart chakra, is also the color associated with prosperity. When we are openhearted we have the grateful, happy, generous, compassionate, open-handed, serviceful qualities that are the hallmark of true prosperity. It is only with genuine, openhearted love that life becomes rich and full.

Once we experience love for ourselves, we can extend that love out to others. Opening our hearts creates the experience of prosperity in several ways. For one thing, when our hearts are open, we feel grateful. When we are grateful, we feel "rich". When we are grateful, we tend to be generous. When we give of the goodness in our hearts, we affirm that we have plenty; we affirm that we are prosperous. People routinely bless those who give to them, so we receive many blessings when we open our hands and hearts.

In this chapter, we examine how love, gratitude, generosity and selfless service create prosperity. There is a story about the importance of tithing and information on how to tithe effectively. Included are a Kundalini Yoga set for the heart chakra, a meditation for blessing others, two meditations for prosperity and sending heart chakra energy to others, and a shabad for gratitude.

When our hearts are open, we "zero" ourselves out. That means we don't let our egos get in the way, and we are willing to make sacrifices for others. When we zero ourselves out, the universe rushes in to fill the vacuum, showering us with every blessing including prosperity.

This is why tithing is important for prosperity. By tithing, we are acknowledging that we have sufficient abundance to give. By tithing, we acknowledge our gratitude to the One who grants us wealth. After all, we can't write thank you letters to God. But we can tithe. And by tithing, we zero ourselves out. We create a vacuum which must be filled and refilled, therefore, we prosper.

Tithing

We tithe as an act of gratitude. We tithe to acknowledge that everything belongs to the Infinite anyway. We tithe to invest in the Infinite so that the Infinite will invest in us.

To tithe is to give one-tenth of whatever we receive back to God. Traditionally we give money, but tithes may also be given in goods, services and time. This tithe should go to wherever you are getting your spiritual juice, not just any charity. If you are a member of a religious tradition, tithe there. If not, then tithe to any spiritual organization you feel good about.

If your spouse does not want to tithe, tithe only from your personal funds. While it is best to give the full tenth of one's gross income, you may feel that this is not possible. Give what you can. I assure you many people feel that they can't afford NOT to tithe.

I once had a student who was in truly desperate straits. She had been out of work for so long that she was no longer eligible for unemployment benefits. She had nearly lost her house, but some friends had prevented foreclosure, and she was now in debt to them. There was a tenant at her house, who was destroying the place rather than fixing it, as he had originally agreed to do. The car she was driving was on its last legs and often wouldn't run.

She gathered with a group of friends to do affirmations and meditations for her prosperity. At first, nothing much changed for her. Then one day, I asked if she tithed. She gave me a sad look and said she had nothing to tithe with. I pulled a dollar out of my wallet and gave it to her. A light went on in her face, and she cheerfully pulled a dollar out of her wallet and sent both dollars off to the spiritual organization of her choice. Soon thereafter, she got a decent job which allowed her to begin paying off her debts as well as cover her basic living expenses. She repaid the dollar to me and she continued to tithe. The destructive tenant left a few months later. She was able to replace her old clunky car with a good quality one. She received a nice nest egg from her father's estate, which she could easily have lost due to legal complications. She never doubted that it was tithing that turned the tide for her.

Yogi Bhajan has said, "Serving, where there's no alternative reward, is the only way to elevate your consciousness. Don't feel stupid about it. Even doing community service to clean the streets, help build a house for someone poor, or doing something for which there is no status and no reward--it is called zero, *shunia*: activity for zero, no reward, not even a thank you. Its reward is hundred-thousand-fold, million-thousand-fold from the heavens. It is called seeding the fortune."

Miracles happen when we open our hearts and share, when we open our hearts and serve. A simple way to open the heart is to breathe very slowly and deeply, mentally vibrating *Saat* on the inhale and extending the sound into Infinity while mentally expanding the heart chakra energy into Infinity as well, and then mentally vibrating *Naam* on the exhale and acknowledging that the Infinite is you. You can do this any time. Here are some other techniques to open the heart and extend love out to others.

KUNDALINI YOGA & MEDITATIONS FOR THE HEART CHAKRA

SET FOR HEART AND SOUL

This set is an excellent practice for opening the heart and staying aligned with the Soul. It also enhances general flexibility and strengthens the nervous system and the navel chakra. It is thus a good practice for green energy and empowerment.

The mantra *Ong So Hang* in exercise 7 is translated "Creator, I am That." This is a mantra for the heart chakra.

1. Sitting in Easy Pose with a straight spine, place the hands in Gyan Mudra on the knees. Inhale in 3 equal parts, hold the breath for a few seconds, exhale in 3 equal parts, and hold the breath out for a few seconds. Continue for 6 minutes.

2. With the legs straight out in front, point the toes and raise the arms up to a 60° angle out to the sides. Raise one leg so the foot is at chest level (or as close as possible). The hands are like antenae drawing in energy. Do Breath of Fire. Continue for 3 minutes. Then inhale. Relax for 1 minute. Repeat on the other side. Continue for 3 minutes. Then inhale. Relax for 3 minute.

3. Back Platform on the Elbows: Lying on the back, raise the body up on the elbows so that the body forms a straight inclined plane with only the heels and elbows touching the ground. The toes are pointed. Hold this position with Breath of Fire. Continue for 3 minutes.

4. Lying on the back, lift the legs together straight up to 90°. Reach up and grab the toes (or the ankles if the hands don't reach the toes). Hold this position with Breath of Fire. Continue for 3 minutes. Then inhale. Relax on the back for 2 minutes.

5. Stand on tiptoe with the arms in front parallel to the ground, palms facing down. Hold this position with Breath of Fire. Continue for 3 minutes. Then inhale slowly and squat down in Crow Pose leaving the arms stretched out in front. Keep the feet flat on the ground. You may need to splay the feet to do this. Hold this position with long, deep breathing. Continue for 1 minute.

6. Cat-Cow: Come onto all fours with the hands directly under the shoulders. The arms and upper legs are parallel to each other and perpendicular to the ground. Inhale and raise the head up and lower the belly. You will look something like a swayback cow. Exhale and lower the head and arch the back up. You will look something like an angry cat. Alternate rapidly between the 2 positions with Breath of Fire. Continue for 1 minute. Then inhale. Relax in Easy Pose for 2 minutes.

7. Yoga Mudra: Sitting in Easy Pose interlace the fingers with the right thumb over the left behind the back. Keeping the arms straight, bring the arms up as high as possible. Focus at the brow point. Bend from the waist so the forehead touches the ground and chant *Ong*. Chant *So Hang* and rise back up.("Hang" is pronounced like the English "Hung.") Continue for 3 minutes.

8. Sitting in Easy Pose, meditate with the hands in Gyan Mudra on the knees. Focus the eyes downward to the heart. Deeply inhale while silently chanting *Sat*. Then deeply exhale while silently chanting *Naam*. Continue for 10 minutes.

MEDITATION FOR BLESSINGS

Practicing this meditation is a noble act. Bless others and in turn be blessed.

Sitting in Easy Pose with a straight spine, extend the right arm in front with arm up at a 45° angle with the palm flat and facing the ground. The arm is relaxed and need not be kept straight. Place the left hand flat on the heart center. Close the eyes and look deep into the navel point. Imagine that you are a noble and angelic being, blessing the universe and all people, good and bad, even those who hate you. Use the word Bless in your mind, constantly and consistently. Let your heart open; feel caring and kind. Continue for 9 minutes. Then bless yourself for 2 minutes. Inhale, hold the breath as long as possible and circulate the blessings throughout your body. Exhale. Repeat this sequence twice for a total of 3 times. Relax.

MEDITATION FOR PROJECTION FROM THE HEART

Practicing the mantra *Aad Guray Nameh, Jugaad Guray Nameh, Sat Guray Nameh, Siri Guru Dayvay Nameh* balances and strengthens all ten Bodies, and brings wisdom and protection. The mantra may be translated, "I bow to the Primal Guru. I bow to the Guru of the Ages. I bow to the True Guru. I bow to the Infinitely Great Divine Guru." This meditation is good for opening the heart chakra and sending the energy of love into the Universe, thus creating the green energy that promotes prosperity.

Sitting in Easy Pose with a straight spine, place the palms together at the heart center with the thumbs crossed, right thumb over left thumb. In a slow monotone chant *Aad Guray Naameh* while extending the arms up to 60° in front. Inhale powerfully and return the hands to the heart center. Chant *Jugaad Guray Naameh* while again extending the arms up to

60° in front. Inhale powerfully and return the hands to the heart center. Chant *Sat Guray Naameh* while again extending the arms up. Inhale powerfully and return the hands to the heart center. Chant *Siree Guroo Dayvay Naameh* while extending the arms up again. As you extend the arms, project the mind out towards infinity. Continue for 11 minutes. (This may be increased by 5 minutes per day up to a maximum of 31 minutes.)

MEDITATION TO RECOGNIZE PROSPERITY

This meditation is similar to the last one with much the same benefits to the heart chakra and ten bodies, but note the subtle differences. Practicing this variation is especially good for helping us to act quickly on opportunities as they arise.

Sitting in Easy Pose with a straight spine, place the hands in Prayer Mudra at the heart center. Raise the arms up to 60° in front while chanting *Aad Guray Nameh*. Bring the hands back to the heart center while chanting *Jugaad Guray Nameh*. Raise the arms up again while chanting *Sat Guray Nameh*. Bring the hands back to the heart center while chanting *Siri Guroo Dayvay Nameh*. Continue for 31 minutes.

SHABAD YOGA: AAGAI PAACHAI KUSAL BHA-I-AA FOR GRATITUDE

Reciting this shabad in the original Gurmukhi creates an incredibly blissful inner state and the experience of joyful, heartfelt gratitude. It makes an excellent affirmation when recited in English. Reciting it promotes green energy and prosperity as we experience the gifts we already have.

Aagai paachai kusal bha-i-aa.
Gur poorai pooree sabh raakhee paarbrahm prabh keenee ma-i-aa.
(Rahaa-o)
Man tan rav rehi-aa har preetam dookh darad sagalaa mit ga-i-aa.
Shaanti sehj aanad gun gaa-ay doot dusht sabh ho-ay kha-i-aa.
Gun avagun prabh kachh na beechaari-o kar kirpaa apunaa kar la-i-aa.
Atul badaa-eee achut abinaasee naanak ucharai har kee ja-i-aa.
Translation:
Ecstasy abounds both here and hereafter
For I am utterly protected by my perfect True Guru.
The One Supreme Lord has extended His mercy unto me.
(Pause)
Every fiber of my being has been filled with the Love of my Lord,
And all my pain and suffering have been mercifully dispelled.
In perfect peace and equipoise the Saints sing forth God's praises,
And all the evil messengers have been annihilated.
He has not rejected me based on my strengths and weaknesses;
My beloved Lord has taken me completely as His own.
His greatness is beyond all measure;
He is imperishable and cannot be moved.
O Nanak, victory has been acclaimed!

   Guru Arjan Dev. Rag Bilawal. Siri Guru Granth Sahib, p.829.

INTUITION AND ANSWERED PRAYERS

"Your supply is equal to your demand. There is no lack of supply, only a lack of demand." Yogi Bhajan

Intuition and prayer form a continuum. When we pray, we broadcast out to the Universe to ask for what we want or to give thanks for what we have. When we are intuitive, we are receiving the messages that the Universe is sending out to us. Thus prayer and intuition may be viewed as two sides of the same coin. For the purposes of prosperity, both are necessary. With prayer we ask. With intuition we receive.

Intuition is that sixth sense that allows us to be in the right place at the right time doing the right thing. Through intuition we understand what is true in ways that transcend the first five senses. It is largely through intuition that we are guided in ways that will answer our prayers, fulfill our dreams, and bring prosperity to ourselves and others.

The focus that allows us to receive information intuitively also allows us to send out signals to the Universe through our

This chapter examines the relationship between intuition and effective prayer, as well as the different types of prayer and the part intuition plays in creating prosperity and answering prayers. Included are a Kundalini Yoga set for improving intuition and four powerful meditations: a meditation for improving intuition, a meditation for strengthening both intuition and the power of the word, a meditation for prosperity and answered prayers, and a meditation for prosperity and intuition. There is also a shabad for fulfilling wishes.

spoken and unspoken words. That means that the more intuitive we become, the more our prayers will be answered. You've heard the expression, "Be careful what you pray for; you may get it!" That goes double when we amp up our intuition.

There are many types of prayer. There are formal prayers which can either be just a routine or which can be a focused and effective form of meditation. There are prayers of gratitude. There are petitionary God-please-take-care-of-me type prayers. There are prayerful conversations with God. And then there's the most effective form of prayer: going quietly inward and acknowledging that God is going to take care of things. This last is the most effective form of prayer. I have never known it to fail.

The practice of any technique in this book will improve intuition and the effectiveness of our prayers to some extent. The following are particularly good techniques for increasing both our intuition and the power of our prayer.

KUNDALINI YOGA & MEDITATION FOR INTUITION AND ANSWERED PRAYERS

BRAIN DOCTOR KRIYA

Practicing this kriya balances the brain, releases tension and frustration, enhances creativity and helps adjust both the ribcage and the lower back. It is a wonderful practice for improving intuition and effective communication, which means that prayers are more likely to be answered.

The mantra *Har Har Har Hari* in Exercises 6 and 8 refers to the creative, abundant aspect of God. It is good for the brain and good for prosperity.

The mantra *Gobinday, Mukanday, Udaaray, Apaaray, Haring, Kariang, Nirnaamay, Akaamay* in Exercise 7 is translated, "Sustainer, Liberator, Enlightener, Infinite, Destroyer, Creator, Nameless, Desireless." This is a mantra for releasing deep-seated blocks. Practicing this mantra also balances the brain, enhances brain function, and strengthens the Radiant Body, which is important for prosperity.

1. Sit in Lotus Pose by bringing the left foot onto the upper right thigh and bringing the right foot over it onto the upper left thigh. If this is not possible, sit in Easy Pose. Place the hands by the hips and use the hands to push the body up and down off the floor. Coordinate this motion with Breath of Fire. Continue for 2 minutes.

2. Lying on the stomach with the forehead on the ground, interlock the hands behind the back. Inhale and raise the head and torso up as high as they will go. Exhale and relax back down. Continue for a total of 52 repetitions.

3. Start from the same position as the last exercise. Inhale, raise the head and torso up as high as possible and strike both heels to the buttocks. Exhale and relax back down. Continue for a total of 52 repetitions, then relax with the arms by the sides.

4. Lying on the back, interlock the hands on the navel. Jump the legs up towards the head, lifting the buttocks off the ground. The head stays relaxed and on the ground. Continue for a total of 52 repetitions.

5. Squat in Crow Pose with the feet flat on the ground. Bring the arms in front parallel to the ground with the palms together. Inhale, stand up and clap the hands over the head. Exhale back down and clap the hands with the arms straight in front. Continue for a total of 52 repetitions.

6. Sitting in Easy Pose, bring the arms straight out to the sides parallel to the ground with the palms facing down. Keep the arms straight and tight throughout the following four-part exercise. First, flap the arms like a bird three times, then slap the ground firmly with the hands. Second, flap the arms three times, then clap the hands above the head. Third, flap the arms three times, then clap the arms in front parallel to the ground. Fourth, flap the arms three times, then clap the hands behind the head. Once the sequence becomes familiar, chant *Har Har Har Hari* in rhythm with the movement. Continue for 2 minutes.

7. Sitting in Easy Pose, repeat the last exercise, but chant *Gobinday, Mukanday, Udaaray, Apaaray, Hariang, Kariang, Nirnaamay, Akaamay* in rhythm with the motion. Continue for 3 minutes.

8. Sitting in Easy Pose, repeat Exercise 6. Continue for 3 minutes.

9. Sitting in Easy Pose, close the eyes and sing any beautiful, uplifting song (or series of songs). You may use a tape as a background (the song Himalaya was used when the class was taught) or sing without accompaniment. Let your body move meditatively in rhythm with the music. Feel yourself soaring. Express yourself. Continue for 5 minutes.

MEDITATION SET TO BECOME INTUITIVE

Practicing this meditation series deeply heals and enriches the mind and mental energy. It gently stimulates the pituitary and counteracts frustration, depression, and computer sickness. It is a wonderful practice for developing the creativity and intuition that make prosperity a living reality. The mantra *Har* used in Exercise 5 refers to the creative, abundant aspect of God and is often used in prosperity meditations.

1. Sitting in Easy Pose, place the left hand on the heart center. Bend the right elbow down by the side and point the index finger straight up with the rest of the fingers in a fist locked down by the thumb. Keep the spine very straight and pulled up so that the weight is off the buttocks. Close the eyes. Inhale slowly and deeply through the nose. Hold the breath, then slowly exhale with a whistle through the mouth. Imagine that your purity and divinity are calling. Contact your own Infinity and feel exalted. Continue for 7 minutes. Inhale deeply and shift into the next position.

2. Sitting in Easy Pose with the spine very straight, place the right hand either just above the head or gently touching the top of it. Bend the left elbow down by the side and point the index finger straight up with the rest of the fingers in a fist locked down by the thumb. Eyes are closed. Breathe in using the same pattern as in Exercise one. Continue for 4 minutes.

3. Sitting in Easy Pose with the spine very straight, bring the palms together overhead with the arms stretched straight up so that there is a stretch in the armpits. Breathe in using the same pattern as in Exercise one. Consciously circulate your energy to rejuvenate yourself. Continue for 2 1/2 minutes.

4. Sitting in Easy Pose with a straight spine, place the right hand on top of the left at the center of the chest. Listen to divine music, such as Singh Kaur's *Rakhe Rakhan Har* tape, or music within you. Relax, breathe, and be. Continue for 3 1/2 minutes.

5. Sitting in Easy Pose with a straight spine, press the hands on the navel point. Close the eyes. Chant *Har* at a rate of about one Har per second. (Simran Kaur Khalsa's *Tantric Har* tape was used in class.) Press the navel forcefully with the hands on each *Har*. Remember to touch the tongue to the upper palate just above the teeth to create the "r" sounds. Continue for 3 minutes. Move directly into the next exercise.

6. Bring the arms up parallel to the ground at shoulder level with the hands grasping opposite elbows. Inhale and hold the breath 5-10 seconds while squeezing the spine and tightening all the muscles of the body. Exhale. Repeat this sequence twice for a total of 3 times.

INDRA NITTRI MEDITATION

"Indra Nittri" means the eyes of Indra. Through the practice of this meditation we become intuitive and all-seeing. All words spoken after practicing this meditation become amplified powerfully. Therefore be very careful what you say and what you pray for when you are practicing this meditation. You can become very prosperous doing this meditation if you take advantage of its creative power and immediately follow it with affirmations or shabads for prosperity.

The mantra *Ek Ong Kaar Sat Gur Prasaad Sat Gur Prasaad Ek Ong Kaar* literally means "One Creator Creation Truth Guru's Gift Truth Guru's Gift One Creator Creation". This mantra may be used to turn negative situations into positive ones and to align you with your soul.

Sitting in Easy Pose, hold the knees firmly with the hands, and lift the chest and spine gently. The eyes are either closed or one-tenth open. Focus at the brow point on the movements of the tongue. Chant in a steady rhythm on one breath *Ek Ong Kaar Sat Gur Prasaad Sat Gur Prasaad Ek Ong Kaar*. Pull in the navel while chanting *Ek Ong*. Release it on *Kaar*. Lift up and pull in on the diaphragm while chanting *Sat Gur*. Release it on *Prasaad*. Remember to touch the tongue to the upper palate just above the teeth to make the "r" sounds. Continue for 11-62 minutes.

Then inhale, hold the breath as long as is comfortable, then relax. (Note: this meditation is not recommended for pregnant women.)

ARDAAS BHAEE MEDITATION

The *Ardaas Bhaee* mantra may be translated, "The prayer that has been made to Guru Amar Das is guaranteed by Guru Ram Das," so this is a mantra for answered prayers. This is also a good meditation for avoiding getting caught in the ego's games. Practicing this meditation helps you consciously connect with your soul, and grants the experience of peace and prosperity.

Many tapes and CDs of this mantra are available through the resources listed in the back of the book. This meditation may be done using any of these tapes/CDs, or you may chant it on your own.

Sitting in Easy Pose with a straight spine, relax the upper arms by the sides and bring the hands up to the level of the heart. Interlace the fingers and the grip tighter than normal. Focus on tip of the nose. Chant *Ardaas Bhaee Amar Daas Guroo, Amar Daas Guroo Ardaas Bhaee, Raam Daas Guroo Raam Daas Guroo, Raam Daas Guroo Sachee Sahee*. Remember to touch the tongue to the upper palate just above the teeth to create the "r" sounds. Time is open.

67

MEDITATION TO TAP OPPORTUNITIES

This is an incredibly powerful meditation. When Yogi Bhajan taught it, he suggested teaching it to someone who is penniless without giving them anything else, then stepping back and watching what happens. I can attest that it works: this is the meditation I was doing when I found the publisher for this book. It enhances intuition so that we can tap opportunities around us and know when we are going in the right direction.

Hariang means Destroyer. That may not sound so wonderful. But in practice what it does is destroy those blocks in our psyches that keep us out of rhythm with the flow of the Universe.

The first exercise is a physical warm-up that may be practiced on its own for 10-15 minutes per day. It is good for the lymph glands and, according to yogic tradition, helps prevent breast cancer, heart attacks, and strokes.

1. Sitting calmly in any comfortable position, relax the arms out to the sides with the palms facing forward. Bring alternate hands up to the heart center without touching the chest. Do not bend the wrists or the hands. Move as rapidly as possible. Time is open. Move directly into the next exercise.

2. Sitting with a straight spine in any comfortable position, bring the sides of the hands together, palms up, at the level of the diaphragm. Keeping the fingers and thumbs relaxed, spread the fingers slightly and bring the thumbs slightly up and out. Look towards the little fingers. Inhale deeply and chant *Hariang* 8 times per breath, emphasizing the "ng" sound. Each breath cycle takes about 10 seconds. Remember to touch the tongue to the upper palate just above the teeth to create the "r" sounds. Continue for 11 minutes.)You may gradually increase the time to 31 minutes.)

3. Sitting with a straight spine in any comfortable position, touch the fingertips together at diaphragm level with the fingers loosely separated and relaxed. The thumb remains extended and separate. Look down at a 60° angle. Inhale deeply and chant *Hariang* 16 times per breath. Each breath cycle will take 13-15 seconds. Continue for 31 minutes. It is also fine to practice it for 11 or 62 minutes.

SHABAD YOGA: JO MAANGEH SHABAD FOR ANSWERED PRAYER

Practicing this shabad helps you fulfill all of your wishes. It also makes a great affirmation.

Chatur disaa keeno bal apanaa sir oopar kar dhaari-o.
Kirpaa kataakh avalokan keeno daas kaa dookh bidaari-o.
Har jan raakhay gur govind.
Kanth laa-i avagun sabh maytay da-i-aal purakh bakhashand.
(Rahaa-o)
Jo maangeh thaakur apanay tay so-ee-so-ee dayvai.
Naanak daas mukh tay jo bolai eehaa oohaa sach hovai.
Translation:
In all four directions, the Lord Himself has extended His Power. Upon my head He has placed His Hand.
With His Eye of Mercy beholding all, He has dispelled the miseries of His servant.
God's slave has been saved by the Guru, the World-Lord.
Drawing me to His Bosom, all my sins are erased by the Forgiving, Compassionate Lord. (Pause)
Whatever I ask of my Lord, that He Himself grants to me.
Whatever slave Nanak utters with his mouth proves True here and hereafter.

Guru Arjan Dev. Rag Dhanaasari. Siri Guru Granth Sahib, p.681-2.

THE RADIANT BODY AND GOLDEN SUCCESS

"No one else can limit you. If you want to limit yourself, you can. Otherwise the entire resources of the Universe are yours to use." Yogi Bhajan

In 1975, a young, personable and open-hearted American couple moved to Hamburg, Germany, to establish a 3HO ashram and teach Kundalini Yoga and meditation. They spoke no German and had no job lined up for them. Their spiritual practice was strong and they trusted that God would arrange things for them, but they were not sure how to support themselves and their two-year-old daughter. They stayed connected to their mission by teaching yoga and sharing what they had learned. They served all who came to them and slowly built a yoga center. They served Yogi Tea to the students, which was a delicious and healing recipe taught by Yogi Bhajan. The students greatly appreciated this bit of yogic knowledge. This gave the couple the idea to cut the tea ingredients into small bits, package the mix and sell it to health food stores. They did this work themselves with the help of anyone who happened to be around who was ready, willing and able to pitch in.

This chapter starts with a story of success and examines how a strong Radiant Body leads to long-term success and prosperity. Included in this chapter are a Kundalini Yoga set for keep-up spirit, two meditations that strengthen the Radiant Body, and two prosperity meditations. Also included is a shabad for prosperity and protection which is the source of a prosperity mantra.

Today, as I am writing this book, the Yogi Tea Company is the largest herbal tea company in the natural foods market in Europe and the second largest in the United States. The company has 30 employees in Europe and is part of a 150-employee corporation in the USA. This does not include their suppliers. The Yogi Tea Company has sponsored organic projects in Third World countries to provide a supply of organic ingredients and support sustainable agriculture in rainforests and other locations.

Also, the Hamburg metropolitan area now has 230 certified Kundalini Yoga teachers. Germany as a whole, which had no 3HO Kundalini Yoga teachers prior to 1975, now has approximately 700 certified Kundalini Yoga teachers with 70-100 new teachers being trained each year.

This is the type of success that is possible when the radiant body is strong. When the radiant body is strong, we have more than enough courage, strength and endurance to keep up in the face of any challenge time and space throws at us; and to come through successfully. When the radiant body is strong, we have the courage to go beyond our circumstances, the courage to succeed, the courage to excel. Funny thing about courage: it means "with heart." So the Radiant Body takes the green energy of the heart and carries it to Infinity.

The radiant body is a body of radiant energy and the light that extends beyond the aura into Infinity. This is the *gold* of our souls that places the call into the Universe. We then give the Universe the space to answer the call in limitless, golden ways. Thus the radiant body is where we are empowered; not by our little selves, but by Infinity.

When we need to face challenges cheerfully and successfully, when we want prosperity that goes beyond anything ordinary, a strong radiant body is the best asset we can have. Here are some particularly good techniques for amping up the radiant body.

KUNDALINI YOGA & MEDITATION FOR THE RADIANT BODY

SET FOR KEEP-UP SPIRIT

Keep-up spirit is the radiant body quality that allows us to come through anything radiantly and cheerfully no matter what setbacks, obstacles, or challenges we face. Practicing this set enhances our radiance so that we don't give up when prosperity is right around the corner. It also enhances general flexibility and strengthens the aura and the sciatic nerve. This is a very energizing set, but easy enough for most beginners.

1. Sitting in Easy Pose, extend the arms up at a 60° angle in front of the body with the hands 2 1/2-3 feet apart, palms facing each other and fingers side by side. Begin a four-part motion. On 1, bend the wrists so that the fingers are parallel to the ground with the palms facing each other. On 2, bend the wrists so that fingers point up with the palms facing each other. On 3, bend the wrists so that the palms face the ceiling. On 4, return the hands to the original position. Move quickly and rhythmically, focusing strongly at the brow point to aid coordination. Continue for 3 minutes.

2. Sitting in Easy Pose, interlace the fingers with the fingers inside the palms with the fingertips of opposite fingers pressed together and the thumbs crossed. Place this mudra at chest level with the palms facing inward. Inhale and stretch the arms out. Exhale and bring them back to the chest. Move powerfully and rapidly. Continue for 3-8 minutes.

3. Alternate leg lifts: Lie on the back with the hands under the lower back, palms down. Inhale and raise the left leg to 90°. Exhale and lower it. Then inhale and raise the right leg to 90°. Exhale and lower it. Keep the legs straight and the toes pointed. Continue for 3-4 minutes.

4. Life Nerve Stretch: Sitting with the legs straight out in front, grab the toes or whatever you can reach, keeping the legs straight. Inhale and stretch up. Exhale, bend from the waist and bring the head to the knees or as far down as it will go. Move and breathe powerfully. Continue for 3 minutes.

5. Cat/Cow: On all fours with the arms and thighs parallel to each other, inhale and arch the spine down and the head up. You will look something like a swayback cow. Exhale and arch the spine up and the head down. You will look something like an angry cat. Keep the arms and legs stationary. Continue for 1-2 minutes.

6. In Cow Pose with the head up and the spine arched down, begin kicking the buttocks very fast and powerfully with alternate heels. Make sure there is padding under the knees and feet. The upper part of the body remains stationary. Continue for 1 minute.

7. Stand up straight with the feet shoulder-width apart and the hands on the hips. Roll the torso in full circles bending from the waist as far as possible in all directions. Move powerfully and quickly. Continue for 2 minutes.

8. Standing with the feet shoulder-width apart, inhale and raise the arms straight up. Then exhale and bring the palms to the ground or as far as they will go, keeping the legs straight. Move powerfully and quickly. Continue for 1 minute.

9. Spread the legs as far apart as possible. Inhale and raise the arms straight up. Exhale and bring the palms to the ground or as far as they will go. Continue for 1 minute.

10. Stand with the feet together. Inhale and raise the arms straight up. Exhale and bring the palms to the ground or as far as they will go without bending the knees. Continue for 2-3 minutes.

11. Standing with the feet shoulder-width apart, place the hands on the shoulders with the fingers pointing towards the neck. Inhale and raise the arms straight up. Exhale and return the hands to the shoulders. Move as fast as possible. Continue for 30 seconds.

75

12. Sitting in Easy Pose, roll the neck in good full circles. Move quickly, but carefully. Continue for 30 seconds.

13. Relax deeply on the back. Continue for  3-10 minutes or more.

KRIYA TO MAGNIFY THE RADIANT BODY

This is a meditation for the radiant body. The practice of this meditation empowers us to be healthy, happy, creative, and prosperous. If the fingers of the left hand are spread as wide as possible and the navel is pulled powerfully, then it also enhances intuition. When Yogi Bhajan taught this meditation, he told a story of a man who came to him in a state of physical collapse. The doctors gave the man three months to live. Yogi Bhajan had the man practice this meditation for 40 days, and the man also made some changes in his diet. At the end of that time, the man was in excellent health. There has been no relapse.

The mantra used is the second half of *Mool Mantra*. It is a mantra of Truth, used to raise the kundalini. The translation is "True in the beginning, True through all times, True even now, Nanak, Truth shall ever be."

Sitting in Easy Pose with a straight spine, spread the fingers of the left hand as wide as possible and place the hand on the heart center with the thumb pointing up. Make a fist of the right hand with the index finger extended and pointing up. Place the right arm by the side with the tip of the index finger at eye level and the palm facing forward. Close the eyes and breath deeply a few times.

Then chant *Aad Sach, Jugaad Sach, Haibee Sach, Naanak Hosee Bhee Sach* pulling the navel powerfully on each *Sach* so that the navel connects with the spine. Time is open. (It was done in class for 8 minutes. Yogi Bhajan stated that different people might need different durations. 11 minutes works well in most situations.) Then inhale and relax.(Note: This meditation is not recommended for pregnant women.)

MEDITATION TO DO WHEN NOTHING ELSE WORKS

This is the meditation to do when faced with serious challenges. The mantra is a classic mantra for the radiant body that is noted for the capacity to break through deep-seated blocks. It is translated, "Sustainer, Liberator, Enlightener, Infinite, Destroyer, Creator, Nameless, Desireless." We don't usually think of it as a prosperity meditation, but like all radiant body meditations, it can work that way.

Sitting in Easy Pose with a straight spine, interlace the fingers inside the palms. Place this mudra at the solar plexus with the palms and fingers pointing up. The thumbs are straight and point forward. Eyes are one-tenth open. Chant *Gobinday, Mukanday, Udaaray, Apaaray, Hariang, Kariang, Nirnaamay, Akaamay* as fast as possible so the words become a single indistinguishable sound current. Continue for 11-31 minutes.

BASIC HAR HAR HAR HAR GOBINDAY MEDITATION

The mantra for this meditation combines the Radiant Body mantra for releasing deep-seated blocks used in the meditation above with *Har*, the creative, "green" aspect of God. This mantra is frequently used in prosperity meditations. Many tapes and CDs of this mantra are available through the resources listed in the back of the book. You may chant along with one of these tapes or chant a cappella.

Sitting in Easy Pose with a straight spine, place the hands on the knees. The mudra varies according to the desired outcome. For releasing obstacles and enhancing intuition, use *Gyan Mudra* with the thumb and the tip of the index finger touching. For enhancing the qualities of purity and piety, use *Shuni Mudra* with the thumb and the tip of the middle finger touching. For improving health, use *Surya Mudra* with the thumb and the tip of the ring finger touching. For experiencing prosperity, wealth, and friendship, use *Buddhi Mudra* with the thumb and the tip of the little finger touching. Focus on the tip of the nose. Chant Har *Har Har Har Gobinday, Har Har Har Har Mukanday, Har Har Har Har Udaaray, Har Har Har Har Apaaray, Har Har Har Har Hariang, Har Har Har Har Kariang, Har Har Har Har Nirnaamay, Har Har Har Har Akaamay.* Remember to pull in the navel slightly with each *Har*, and to touch the tongue to the upper palate just above the teeth to make the "r" sounds. Continue for 11-31 minutes.

MAGNIFICENT MANTRA PROSPERITY MEDITATION

This is one of my favorite meditations. It is fun to do, lifts the spirits quickly, and is very effective. It is also a good practice for health and protection.

Sitting in Easy Pose with a straight spine, bend the upper arms down by the sides and bring the hands up comfortably at shoulder level in front of you. Chant *Har Har Har Har Gobinday, Har Har Har Har Mukanday, Har Har Har Har Udaaray, Har Har Har Har Apaaray, Har Har Har Har Hariang, Har Har Har Har Kariang, Har Har Har Har Nirnaamay, Har Har Har Har Akaamay,* making quick fists of the hands and opening them again each time you chant *Har*. Remember to pull in the navel slightly on each *Har* and to touch the tongue to the upper palate just above the teeth to create the "r" sounds. Continue for 11 or 31 minutes.

SHABAD YOGA: AAP SAHAA-EE HO-AA SHABAD FOR THE RADIANT BODY AND PROSPERITY

The *Aap Sahaa-ee Ho-aa* mantra is derived from this shabad. Practicing the mantra enhances prosperity and protection. Practicing the shabad also strengthens the Radiant Body and melts the animosity of others. Many tapes and CDs of the mantra, some of which also include the rest of the shabad, are available through the resources listed in the back of the book.

Aithai othai rakhavaalaa.

Prabh satigur deen da-i-aalaa.

Daas apanay aap raakhay.

Ghat ghat shabad subhaakay.

Gur kay charan oopar bal jaa-ee.

Dinas rain saas saas samaalee pooran sabhanee thaa-ee. (Rahaa-o)

Aap sahaa-ee ho-aa.

Sachay daa sachaa dho-aa.

Tayree bhagat vadi-aa-ee

Paa-ee naanak prabh saranaa-ee.

Translation:

Here and hereafter the Lord is my Protector.

The Divine True Guru is merciful to the humble.

The Lord Himself protects His servants.

In each and every heart His beautiful sound current resounds.

Unto the Guru's Lotus Feet, I am a sacrifice.

Day and night, with every breath, I remember the One Who is pervading everywhere. (Pause)

The Lord Himself has become my Refuge and Protector.

True is the Support of the True Lord.

In devotion to You, O Lord, lies greatness.

Nanak has obtained greatness by seeking Your Shelter, O Lord.

Guru Arjan Dev. Rag Sorath. Siri Guru Granth Sahib, p.628.

THE SPIRIT OF PROSPERITY:
LIVING FROM THE SOUL

"Prosperity, relationships and strength grow from tranquility,"
Yogi Bhajan

We begin with the soul, and we end with the soul. This is true of our lives, and it is also true of prosperity. The soul provides the initial creative spark from which the rest of our destiny unfolds. When we follow the call of the soul, we begin the path that leads to true prosperity and fulfillment.

When I went away to college in 1970, my hope was to get an "Mrs." degree. Although I was good at academics, I was also fed up with them and wanted out. I attended University of California, Santa Cruz, which in those days could have been called "hippie central." In the spring term of my freshman year, I enrolled in a folk dancing class, hoping to find a good man. Unfortunately, I ended up dancing either with the creepiest guy there or another girl.

One day, I decided to go to class and just enjoy dancing with whomever I ended up with as a partner. I felt so enthused with this idea of letting go that I left for class even earlier than usual, completely forgetting that class was going to start 15 minutes late that week. As I neared the gym, I noticed a man who had an almost military gait,

The focus of this chapter pertains to the guidance of the soul and how to maintain the soul connection to enhance prosperity and fulfillment. Included are a Kundalini Yoga set for staying connected to our core self, a meditation for guidance, a meditation for staying connected to our Source, and a prosperity meditation for the soul connection, plus a shabad for the soul connection.

extremely short hair, and an angular face emphasized by dark, square glasses. I thought, "What a funny looking character! I wonder if he's going to try to sell me Bibles."

Meanwhile, the man, who had missed class the previous week and didn't know this one would be starting late, looked over at me with my long hair and bright red jacket and thought, "Gee, what a funny looking character!" When we arrived at the gym, no one else was there. We started a conversation and discovered we had the same sense of humor. Naturally we were dance partners. I got the inner message to leave with him when he left, although I had planned on staying for the next class. We ended up getting to know one another at the one restaurant on campus until they threw us out. That is how I met my future husband.

Jim and I have been married for more than 29 years. On down the road, I became a Sikh and Kundalini Yoga teacher. My husband reconnected with the liberal Protestant Christianity of his childhood. We have a wonderful, supportive marriage. My husband has encouraged me during the process of writing this book and with many other important soul-fulfilling projects in my life.

This is what can happen when we heed the soul's messages. Note that both ideas my soul gave me filled me with joy and ended up fulfilling not just one deep-seated desire, but many An idea that gives you a sick, unhappy feeling doesn't come from your soul. Following the soul's messages doesn't mean taking up a begging bowl or living in a cave. Your soul, after all, is on your side. Instead, it means increased fulfillment and prosperity because it is through our souls that we connect to our Source. The expression "follow your bliss" means to live from your soul.

Kundalini Yoga & Meditation for the Soul Connection

Set to Experience Your Elementary Personality

This is a wonderful set for connecting with our soul and core truth. Practicing this set also reduces stress, strengthens the nervous system, and charges the magnetic field.

Exercise 5 was originally taught using the tape Punjabi Drums. Other rhythmic, elevating music may be substituted.

1. Sitting in Easy Pose, bring the upper arms near the sides and bend the elbows so the forearms point up. Make a "V" of the index and middle fingers, locking the other fingers down with the thumbs. Open and close the V rapidly while focusing on the tip of the nose. Continue for 11 minutes. Then inhale deeply and exhale completely 3 times.

2. Sitting in Easy Pose, interlace the fingers behind the neck. Keeping the spine and neck straight and the elbows out to the sides, close the eyes and do a rapid Breath of Fire. Continue for 3 minutes. Then inhale, hold the breath and stretch every muscle of the body while staying in the position. Repeat this sequence 2 more times for a total of 3 times.

3. Sitting in Easy Pose, interlace fingers in front of the chest. Moving energetically, hit the lap with the joined hands, then hit the chest, then punch up to the sky feeling a stretch in the armpits. Continue for 3 minutes. Inhale deeply and relax.

83

4. Sitting in Easy Pose, bend the right arm so that the upper arm is near the ribs and the forearm points up with the palm facing forward. Place the left hand on the heart and sit in bliss. Breathe long and deep. Consciously love yourself unconditionally. Let that unconditional love take away all insecurities, fear, jealously, and shallowness. Continue for 2 minutes.

5. Stand up and dance rhythmically and vigorously. Continue for 11 minutes.

6. Sitting in Easy Pose, raise the hands over the head. Circle the arms and rotate the upper body on the pelvis. Continue for 2 minutes.

7. Sitting in Easy Pose, whistle a song. Continue for 1 minute.

MEDITATION FOR GUIDANCE

This meditation is a variation of the mantra we use for tuning in. Use it for the soul's guidance and perspective for your personal situation. It is also good for keeping the ego out of the way.

Sitting in Easy Pose with the spine straight, make a cup of the hands with the sides of the palms together. The index finger and thumb form Gyan Mudra. Place this cup at the level of the heart with the upper arms relaxed by the sides. Chant Ong Namo Guroo Dayv Namo Guroo Dayv Namo Guroo Dayv-aa 3-5 times on a single breath, keeping the number of repetitions constant for each breath. As with the mantra for tuning in, "Dayv" is chanted a minor third higher than the rest of the mantra. Continue for 11-31 minutes, or longer if you wish.

MEDITATION TO CONNECT WITH YOUR SOURCE

This is a meditation to experience our inner purity and to realize that God is the One who Creates through us. The mantra is an untranslatable utterance linking the ecstasy of the Infinite and the ecstasy of the soul.

When Yogi Bhajan taught this meditation, he said, "Your power is how simple, straight and pure, how honest, trustworthy and reliable you are. Your own actions will decide whether your purity, piety, future, God, your prosperity and you are near you or far away from you. Watch your purity. See how many good things come to you. Do it for 40 days."

This meditation was originally taught using the Waa-hay Guroo Waa-hay Jeeo section of the Raga Sadhana tape/CD by Sangeet Kaur and Harjinder Singh which is available through the resources listed in the back of the book. If this tape/CD is not available, you may chant without accompaniment or with another musical version of this mantra.

1. Sitting in Easy Pose with a straight spine, extend the arms in front, parallel to the ground with the palms facing down and the hands in Gyan Mudra with the tip of the index finger and the thumb touching and the other fingers stretched as far apart as possible. Keep the elbows straight. Focus on the tip of the nose. Chant Waa-hay Guroo, Waa-hay Guroo, Waa-hay Guroo, Waa-hay Jeeo pulling the navel up and in on each Waa-hay. Remember to touch the tongue to the upper palate just above the teeth on each "r" sound. Continue for 11 minutes.

2. Place the hands on the heart center and keep chanting. Continue for 3 minutes.

3. Leaving the hands on the heart center, chant in a powerful whisper. Continue for 2 minutes.

4. Keep chanting in a powerful whisper and bring the hands to the navel, pressing deeply. Continue for 2 minutes.

5. Maintaining the position and the pressure on the navel, inhale and exhale powerfully through the mouth while listening to the chant silently. Continue for 2 minutes.

6. Still maintaining the pressure on the navel, whistle the chant loudly. Continue for 2 minutes.

Then inhale deeply, hold the breath, and exhale through the mouth with a strong cannon fire breath 3 times. Relax.

SOUL'S BLESSING PROSPERITY MEDITATION

Practicing this meditation elevates the energy and the spirits so that you may experience your soul blessing you with prosperity.

The mantra Har Har Har Har, Waa-hay Guru, Sat Naam, Har Haree can be translated, "The creative, creative, creative aspect of God. Wow! Ecstasy! This Truth is our Identity. This creativity of God." (This meditation is not recommended for pregnant women.)

Sitting in Easy Pose with a straight spine, place the hands on the knees in Gyan Mudra. Eyes are 1/10th open. On a single breath, chant Har Har Har Har and focus on the navel while pulsing the navel on each Har, chant Waa-hay Guru and focus on the heart while pulling up and in on the diaphragm and in on the navel, leave the diaphragm and navel pulled in and chant Sat Naam as you focus on the throat and bring the neck in line with the rest of the spine, chant Har and focus at the brow point, chant Haree and focus at the top of the head allowing the eyes to look upwards a bit. Then relax all tension, inhale and repeat the cycle. Remember to touch the tongue to the upper palate while chanting the "r" sounds. Allow yourself to be absorbed in the sound as you chant. Continue for 11-31 minutes.

SHABAD YOGA: AAPEH MAYL LA-AY FOR THE SOUL CONNECTION

I like practicing this shabad in conjunction with whatever prosperity meditation I happen to be doing to insure that I stay in a soul-centered space. Practicing this shabad is excellent for staying connected to our Divine Source and for releasing attachments to ego and duality.

Aapeh mayl la-ay.

Jab tay saran tumaree aa-ay tab tay dokh ga-ay. (Rahaa-o)

Taj abhimaan ar chint biraanee saadheh saran pa-ay.

Jap jap naam tumaaro preetam tan tay rog kha-ay.

Mahaa mugadh ajaan agi-aanee raakhay dhaar da-ay.

Kaho Naanak guru pooraa bhayti-o aavan jaan rahay.

Translation:

The Lord Himself has blended me into Himself.

Since I came to Your Sanctuary, my sins have been taken away. (Pause)

Shedding my pride and other anxieties, I have sought the saints' protection.

Chanting and meditating on Your Name, O Beloved, diseases are eliminated from my body.

The utterly foolish, ignorant and unwise persons are mercifully saved by the Lord.

Says Nanak: I have met with the Perfect Guru; my comings and goings have ended.

Guru Arjan Dev. Rag Bilawal. Siri Guru Granth Sahib, p.829.

The Prosperity Collection

'"Count blessings, not curses. Actually speaking, there is no easier way to a rich, prosperous, fulfilled life, provided you start living gracefully. Answering the call of duty is the grace, and that grace is what brings you prosperity, completion, value and virtue.'" Yogi Bhajan

The first story is a Buddhist joke/parable I read many years ago. A disciple set out to see his master. He came to a wide and deep river. He sat down by the side of the river and meditated for seven years. At the end of that time, he got up and walked across the surface of the river. When he finally arrived at his master's dwelling place, he exclaims, "Master! As I was traveling to meet you, I came to a wide river. I sat down and meditated for seven years, and then I walked across the river!" Whereupon his Master says, "What a pity you didn't have the money to pay for the ferry!"

> This chapter starts with two stories about prosperity. It contains a Kundalini Yoga set for prosperity, five prosperity meditations, and a particularly powerful shabad for prosperity.

The second story is about Guru Nanak, founding teacher of the Sikh religion. In this story, two men who are neighbors and good friends hear that Guru Nanak is in town. They decide to avail themselves of this opportunity and set out to see him. As they are walking, they notice a very attractive prostitute. One of the men decides that she is much more interesting than the Guru is going to be, so he goes off with her. The other man proceeds to visit Guru Nanak. Each day the men follow this pattern: the one goes off with the prosti-

89

tute and the other proceeds to see Guru Nanak. One day, the man who has been visiting the prostitute receives a valuable gold coin. That same day, the man who has been visiting Guru Nanak has his hand pricked with a large, painful thorn. The man who has just had his hand hurt goes to Guru Nanak and asks why he has just been punished and his friend has just been rewarded. Guru Nanak laughs and says, "Your friend was supposed to have received a large fortune, but because of the way he has been behaving, that fortune has been reduced to a single coin. You were supposed to have been impaled, but because of your devotion, that has been reduced to the mere prick of the hand."

Remembering that we are spirits having a human experience, meditating and living with devotion are ways to lighten our lives, release the burdens and achieve joyful prosperity. But these things do not prevent the experience of pain. The idea promoted in some New Age circles that we create all our pain through negative thinking is inaccurate. We make ourselves miserable with negative thinking and negative, less-than-wholesome actions. But pain is part of the deal that goes with human embodiment.

So use these techniques and allow the Universe to bless you in unexpected ways. Allow miracles to happen. Allow yourself to prosper. Know that you are worthy to have what it takes to pay the ferrymen in life so you can reach your destiny and your destination. But do not judge how well you are doing by comparing yourself with others. Results DO vary with individuals. Be you. You are valuable, and your experience is valuable too...all of it.

KUNDALINI YOGA & MEDITATION FOR PROSPERITY
SET FOR OPPORTUNITY AND GREEN ENERGY

The practice of this prosperity set opens the heart chakra and stimulates the crown chakra. This makes it possible for us to attract those opportunities that are in harmony with our souls.

The mantra *Ong So Hang* in exercise 6 is a mantra for the heart chakra. *Ong* is the creative energy of God (or the Universe, if you prefer). *So Hang* means I am Thou. Remember that Hung has a nasal accent on the "ng".

The mantra *Hari Hari Hari Har* in Exercise eleven utilizes words for the creative, abundant aspect of God.

1. Spinal Flexes: Sitting on the heels with the hands on the thighs, inhale and flex the spine forward while mentally chanting Sat and focusing at the base of the spine. Exhale and flex the spine backwards while mentally chanting Naam and focusing at the navel chakra. Keep the head on the level so it doesn't flop. Continue for 2-3 minutes. Then inhale with the spine straight and apply Root Lock. Exhale, apply Root Lock and hold the breath out for 10 seconds. Repeat this sequence 2 times more.

2. Body drops: With the legs stretched out in front, place the hands on the ground by the hips and lift your body, including the heels, off the ground, then let it drop down. Continue rapidly for 2-3 minutes.

3. Crow pose: Squat down, keeping the feet flat on the ground. Place the arms straight in front with the fingers interlaced and the index fingers extended out pointing to infinity in front of the heart. Hold this position with Breath of Fire. Continue for 2-3 minutes, then inhale, hold the breath, project out from the heart, and exhale.

4. Run in place bringing the knees up high and punching out with alternate fists. Continue vigorously for 3-5 minutes.

5. Kundalini Lotus: Holding the big toes (or the ankles or lower legs if the toes are not possible), balance on the buttocks, keeping the back, legs and arms straight. Hold this position with Breath of Fire. Continue for 2-3 minutes, then inhale, hold the breath, draw the energy up the spine. Exhale and relax.

6. Sitting on the left heel, place the right foot on the left thigh. Cup the hands below the navel, lift the diaphragm, and chant *Ong So Hang* focusing strongly at the heart chakra.("Hang" is pronounced like the English "Hung.") Time is not specified.

7. Sitting in Easy Pose, place the arms out to the sides, parallel to the ground, with the palms facing up. Focus on the energy of the hands, sending the energy in an arc overhead from the left palm to the right, and from the left palm through the arms and shoulders to the right palm. Continue with Breath of Fire for 2-3 minutes, then inhale, hold the breath, continue arcing the energy from the right palm to the left and coursing through the shoulders back to the right. Exhale and relax.

8. Sitting in Easy Pose, place the hands in Venus Lock behind the neck. Exhale and bow the forehead to the ground while mentally chanting *Sat*. Then inhale up mentally chanting *Naam*. Continue for 2-3 minutes.

9. Sitting in Easy Pose, place the arms straight out in front with the palms down. Inhale and raise the right arm up to 60°. Exhale and lower it. Then inhale left arm up and exhale down. The pace is rapid, almost a Breath of Fire. Continue for 2-3 minutes, then

inhale, hold the breath and hold both arms up at the level of the brow point. Project out from the sixth chakra to Infinity. Exhale and relax.

10a. Shakti Pose: Sitting in Easy Pose, place the hands in Venus lock 4 inches above the top of the head with the palms facing down. Focus the eyes upward towards the crown chakra, do Breath of Fire, and allow the energy to project out the top of the head. Continue for 2-3 minutes.

b. Leaving the hands in place, point the index fingers straight up. Focus in the same way with long, deep breathing. Continue for 2-3 minutes.

c. Leaving the hands over the head, bring the fingertips together with the palms apart to form a teepee. Focus in the same way while doing Breath of Fire. Continue for 2-3 minutes. Then inhale, hold the breath, and project the energy out the top of the head. Exhale and relax.

11. Sitting in Easy Pose, relax the arms by the sides and bend the forearms up with the palms flat and facing forward.

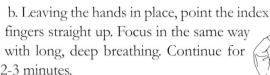

Visualize green energy and chant *Hari Hari Hari Har* from the heart, pulling the navel slightly with each word of the mantra. Remember to pronounce the "r" sounds by flicking the tongue to the upper palate just above the teeth. Continue for 2-11 minutes. Then inhale, exhale and relax with the hands on the knees in Gyan Mudra. Meditate on all your blessings. Feel gratitude. Know yourself to be worthy. Feel a shower of energy come to you. Love yourself. Love your breath. Love everything, known and unknown.

SUBAGH KRIYA

Subagh means good fortune. Yogi Bhajan says about this kriya, "Even if God has written with His own hand, that you shall live under misfortune, by doing Subagh Kriya you can turn your misfortune into prosperity, fortune and good luck."

The first two exercises were originally taught using Simran Kaur Khalsa's Tantric Har tape which is available through the resources listed in the back of this book. *Har* refers to the creative, green energy aspect of God.

The mantra *Har Haray Haree Waa hay Guru* used in Exercise 4 is a mantra of the ecstatic experience of the creative, green energy aspect of the Creator. It is often used in prosperity meditations.

All five parts of this kriya must be done for equal lengths of time: either 3 minutes or 11 minutes. Never exceed 11 minutes per exercise. Only the first exercise of this kriya may be practiced separately from the other exercises. It is a powerful prosperity meditation in its own right. In fact, it is so powerful that Yogi Bhajan suggests doing it for only 3 minutes if you are employed; the longer time is for people who are unemployed

1. Sitting in Easy Pose with a straight spine, bend the elbows down by the sides with the upper arms relaxed and place the palms face up in front of the chest. Focus on the tip of the nose. First strike the sides of the hands together from the base of the little fingers to the base of the palms. Then turn your hands over and strike the sides of the index fingers together. Alternate these two positions, striking hard at a rate of about 1 strike per second. Chant *Har* with each strike of the hands, pulling slightly on the navel and touching the tip of the tongue to the upper palate just above the teeth.

94

2. Sitting in Easy Pose with a straight spine, stretch the arms up at a 60° angle keeping the arms straight. With the palms facing forward, spread the fingers as wide and stiff as they will go. Crisscross the arms in front of the face. The left arm first crosses in front of the right, and then the right crosses in front of the left. Continue alternately crossing the arms, keeping the arms straight and the fingers spread wide and stiff. Move at a rate of about 1 crossing per second, silently vibrating *Har* each time the arm crosses.

3. Sitting in Easy Pose with a straight spine and with the arms still up at a 60° angle, make fists with the thumbs inside, squeezing the thumbs as if to squeeze out all the blood from them. Move the arms in small backwards circles, keeping the elbows straight and maintaining the pressure on the thumbs. Chant *God* powerfully from the navel, 1 repetition of *God* with each backward circle, at a rate of 1 backward circle per second. Move so powerfully that the spine shakes.

4. Sitting in Easy Pose with a straight spine, bend the arms so that the forearms are parallel to the ground around diaphragm level with the palms facing in and with the left hand inside and the right hand outside. Move the right hand up a few inches and the left down a few inches. Then move the left hand up a few inches and the right down a few inches. Chant *Har Haray Haree Wah-hay Guroo* in rhythm with this alternating motion, in a deep monotone from the navel, at a rate of 1 repetition of mantra every 4 seconds.

If you are practicing the exercises for 11 minutes each, then chant the mantra out loud for 6 minutes, whisper it powerfully for 3 minutes, and whistle it for 2 minutes. If you are practicing the exercises for 3 minutes each, then chant out loud for 1 minute, whisper powerfully for 1 minute, and whistle for 1 minute.

5. Sitting in Easy Pose with a straight spine and the arms held parallel to the ground at shoulder height, rest the right forearm on the left forearm with the palms facing down. Close the eyes. Be very calm and steady. Inhale for 20 seconds, hold for 20 seconds, and exhale for 20 seconds, or as slowly and deeply as possible, inhaling, holding and exhaling for approximately equal lengths of time.

GREEN GOD PROSPERITY MEDITATION

Many people have reported dramatic increases in income or assets after doing this meditation for 40 days or more. My own experience is that practicing this meditation freed me from a deeply ingrained fear of success. I used to feel very uneasy every time I would count my blessings. While doing this meditation for 120 days, I realized that I was harboring the very ancient fear that "the gods would get me" if I became too successful. Seeing that fear allowed me to drop it and allow considerably more good into my life than ever before.

Har is the name for the creative, abundant aspect of God. It is sometimes translated "Green God."

Sitting in Easy Pose with a straight spine, touch the thumbs to the mounds just below the little finger. (This is the mound of Mercury.) Fold the fingers over the thumbs of both hands and make fists. With the forearms parallel to the ground at the level of the heart center, place the fists 1 inch apart from each other with the palms facing down. Focus on the tip of the nose. Chant *Har* 4 times out loud and 4 times in a whisper, pulling the navel slightly on each *Har* and touching the tongue to the upper palate just above the teeth to pronounce the "r" sounds. Continue for 11-31 minutes.

A FUN PROSPERITY MEDITATION

Har Haray Haree Waa Hay Guru is the mantra used in this meditation. It is a mantra of the indescribable and ecstatic experience of God's creativity and abundance. It is, therefore, often used in prosperity meditations. The tape of this mantra by Hari Bhajan Kaur, available through the resources listed in the back of this book, may be used as a background for this meditation, or it may be done without accompaniment.

Sit in Easy Pose with a straight spine. Starting with the hands in Prayer Mudra at the heart center, swing the hands down quickly to the navel, then swing the hands apart with the palms facing forward and the hands out to the sides. Then swing the hands back into prayer mudra. The eyes are one-tenth open, focused on the tip of the nose. Chant *Har Haray Haree Waa Hay Guru* as follows: *Har*–swing the hands down and out to the sides. *Haray*–swing the hands back to Prayer Mudra at the Heart Center. *Haree*–swing the hands down and out to the sides. *Waa*–swing the hands back to Prayer Mudra at the Heart Center. *Hay*–swing the hands down and out to the sides. *Guru*–swing the hands back into prayer mudra at the Heart Center.

Remember to touch the tongue to the upper palate just above the teeth for all the r sounds. Continue for 11 minutes. Then inhale, exhale and relax.

MEDITATION FOR GURPRASAAD

Gurprasaad means gift of the Guru. This is a very easy and relaxing meditation. It is good for developing the quality of receptivity.

With the spine straight, sit cross-legged or in a chair with the feet flat on the ground. Cup the hands with the palms facing up and the sides of the hands together. Press the upper arms comfortably against the ribcage, and bring the mudra up to the level of the heart. Start with the eyes one-tenth open, and allow them to close during the meditation. Experience the boundless flow of spirit. Feel yourself showered with all possible blessings…health, wealth, happiness, and all the best inner qualities. Allow yourself to ask and allow yourself to receive as the spirit moves you. The time is open.

MEDITATION FOR ABUNDANCE

You will need an orange for this meditation. About this meditation, Yogi Bhajan has said, "Feel yourself holding your abundance. The hand is your spirit. It is not a hand you are holding; it is Jupiter, Saturn, Sun, and Mercury. The best thing is to know what you have. Sometimes we do not have the power to concentrate and we miss the opportunity. Elementary abundance is in your hand. Your hands will hold it, the breath of life, the breathing (prana) will be the longest and maximum and you will concentrate. That is all that is needed." As a variation, you may practice Exercises 2 and 3 only. This is recommended if you are doing this meditation for 40 days.

1. Make a fist of the left hand with the thumb holding down the fingers. Wrap the right hand around the fist and place this mudra 6-8 inches in front of the heart center with the palms facing down. Close the eyes. Breathe as long and deep as possible. Continue for 17 minutes.

2. Now hold the orange in the left hand with the right hand over it and palms facing down 6-8 inches in front of the heart center. Hold the orange as a symbol of prosperity and abundance. Focus on the tip of the nose. Breathe long and deep. Continue for 7 minutes.

3. Peel the orange and eat it slowly and carefully, tasting the essence of prosperity as you chew.

Shabad Yoga: the 25th Pauri of Japji Sahib for Prosperity

This is one of the most powerful and effective prosperity technologies available. Eleven consecutive repetitions per day strengthen the radiant body, clear out the subconscious, and allow the flow of all blessings.

Japji Sahib is a lengthy poetic prayer that has an elevating vibration which aligns us with our souls. A *pauri* is a stanza. Several musical versions of this pauri are available through the resources listed in the back of this book. There are also several tapes and CDs available of the entire *Japji Sahib*.

Bahutaa karam likhi-aa na jaa-i.

Vadaa daataa till na tamaa-i.

Kaytay mangeh jodh apaar.

Kayti-aa ganat nahee veechaar.

Kaytay khap tuteh vaykaar.

Kaytay lai lai mukar paa-eh

Kaytay moorkh khaahee khaa-eh.

Kayti-aa dookh bhookh sad maar.

Ay-eh bhi daat tayree daataar.

Band khalaasee bhaanai ho-i.

Hor aakh na sakai ko-i.

Jay ko khaa-ik aakhan paa-i.

Oho jaanai jaytee-aa mu-eh khaa-i.

Aapay jaanai aapay day-i.

Aakheh si bhi kay-ee kay-i.

Jis no bakhsay sifat salaah.

Naanak paatishaahee paatishaaho.

Translation:

The Lord's Blessings are so abundant they cannot be recorded.

The Great Giver keeps nothing for Himself.

Many are the warriors who beg at His Door.

So many, beyond counting, ponder over Him.

Many wither away to death in wickedness.

Many take and take again what is given, and then deny their Creator.

Many are the fools who continue devouring.

Many endure distress, deprivation and perpetual punishment.

Even these are Your Gifts, O Great Giver!

Liberation from bondage comes from God's Will.

No one else has any say in it.

If any fool dares to intervene against God's Will,

He shall know this: how many lashes he shall receive on his face!

The Lord Himself is the Knower; He Himself is the Giver.

Few are they who acknowledge His Gifts.

The one upon whom the Lord bestows His Praises and Eulogies,

O Nanak, is the king of kings.

Guru Nanak Dev ji. Japji Sahib. Siri Guru Granth Sahib, p.5.

GLOSSARY

Aad Guray Nameh, Jugaad Guray Nameh, Sat Guray Nameh, Siri Guru Dayvay Nameh: I call upon the primal Guru, I call upon the Guru of the Ages, I call upon the True Guru, I call upon the Infinitely Great Divine Guru; mantra for protection and knowledge, sometimes used in prosperity meditations

Aad Sach, Jugaad Sach, Haibee Sach, Naanak Hosee Bhee Sach: True in the beginning, True through all times, True even now, Truth shall ever be; the second half of Mool Mantra, used to raise the kundalini and achieve the Truth

Aap Sahaee Hoaa Sachay Daa Sachaa Dhoaa, Har Har Har: The Lord Himself has become our Protector. The Truest of the True has taken care of us. God, God, God; mantra for prosperity and protection

Adi: Primal

Arcline: Halo; men and women both have an arcline that extends over the head from ear to ear; women have a second arcline that extends across the heart center from nipple to nipple

Ardaas Bhaee Amar Daas Guroo Amar Daas Guroo Ardaas Bhaee, Raam Daas Guroo Raam Daas Guroo Raam Daas Guroo Sachee Sahee: The prayer that has been made to Guru Amar Das is guaranteed by Guru Ram Das; mantra for prosperity, answered prayers and releasing the ego's games

Ashram: Literally, a forest dwelling; actually a place where spiritual people teach and sometimes live

Aura: Electro-magnetic field

Buddhi Mudra: Mudra for communication, friendship and prosperity; the tip of the thumb touches the tip of the little finger (Mercury finger)

Chakra: Literally, wheel or circle; one of eight vortices of energy located on or around the body

Dasvandh: Sikh form of tithing

Diaphragm Lock: Done (on an empty stomach only) by lifting the chest and pulling the diaphragm and upper abdominal area in and up on the exhale; helps to open the heart chakra and balance the emotions; also good for the intestines; not recommended for pregnant women

Dhiaan: Deep meditation

Ek Ong Kaar: One Creator Creation

Ek Ong Kaar-a, Sat-a Naam-a, Siri Waa-a Hay Guroo: Literally, One Creator Creation, Truth Name, Infinitely Great Wow! Indescribable Ecstasy Wisdom; mantra for opening and balancing all the chakras and for absorption in ecstasy

Ek Ong Kaar, Sat Naam, Kartaa Purkh, Nirbhao, Nirvair, Akaal Moorat, Ajooni, Saibang, Gurprasaad, Jap, Aad Sach, Jugaad Sach, Haibee Sach, Naanak Hosee Bhee Sach: Literally, One Creator Creation, Truth Name, Doer Being, Without Fear, Without Revenge, Undying Image, Unborn, By Itself, Guru's Gift, Meditate! In the Beginning True, Through the Ages True, Even Now True, Nanak, It Shall Ever Be True; Mool Mantra; mantra for aligning with the Soul and balancing all 10 Bodies

Ek Ong Kaar Sat Gur Prasaad Sat Gur Prasaad Ek Ong Kaar: Literally, One Creator Creation Truth Guru's Gift Truth Guru's Gift One Creator Creation; mantra for turning negative situations into positive ones and for intuition and aligning with the Soul

Gobinday, Mukanday, Udaaray, Apaaray, Hariang, Kariang, Nirnaamay, Akaamay: Sustainer, Liberator, Enlightener, Infinite, Destroyer, Creator, Nameless, Desireless; mantra for the Radiant Body, used to break deep-seated blocks, including blocks to prosperity

Gurmukhi: Literally, from the mouth of the Guru; the language and script used in the Siri Guru Granth Sahib

Gurprasaad: Gift of the Guru

Guru: One who provides the technology to release the darkness and experience the Light

Guru Amar Das: Third Sikh Guru in human embodiment; worked to eliminate the caste system, the immolation of widows and inequality of women; died in 1574 AD at an advanced age

Guru Arjan Dev: Fifth Sikh Guru in human embodiment; the son of Guru Ram Das; prolific poet and compiler of the Siri Guru Granth Sahib; martyred in 1606 AD

Guru Gobind Singh: Tenth and last Sikh Guru in human embodiment; a great warrior/saint and poet; turned the Guruship over to the Siri Guru Granth Sahib; assassinated in 1708

Guru Nanak Dev ji: also Guru Nanak: first and founding Guru of Sikhism; born in 1469 AD; author of Japji; all succeeding Gurus in the Sikh tradition, except for the last one, signed their poetry with his name

Guru Ram Das: Fourth Sikh Guru in human embodiment; called the Guru of miracles because he was an orphan who rose to become the Guru purely on the basis of his devotion and selfless service; died in 1581 AD

Guru Tegh Bahadur: Ninth Sikh Guru in human embodiment; father of Guru Gobind Singh; gave his life in 1675 so that members of another religion might worship God in their own way in peace

Gyan: Knowledge

Gyan Mudra: Mudra for knowledge and intuition; the tip of the thumb touches the index finger (Jupiter finger)

Har: God, specifically the abundant, creative aspect of God; mantra used in prosperity meditations

Har Haray Haree Waa Hay Guroo: Literally, God, God projected out, God in Action, Wow! Indescribable Ecstasy Wisdom; mantra used in prosperity meditations, also used for protection and answered prayers

Har Har Har Har Gobinday, Har Har Har Har Mukanday, Har Har Har Har Udaaray, Har Har Har Har Apaaray, Har Har Har Har Hariang, Har Har Har Har Kariang, Har Har Har Har Nirnaamay, Har Har Har Har Akaamay: Literally, God God God God Sustainer, God God God God Liberator, God God God God Enlightener, God God God God Infinite, God God God God Destroyer, God God God God Creator, God God God God Nameless, God God God God Desireless; mantra used in prosperity meditations

Har Har Har Har Waa-hay Guru Sat Naam Har Haree: Literally, creative, abundant God God God God Wow! Indescribable Ecstasy Wisdom Truth Name God God in Action; mantra used in prosperity meditations

Har Har Har Hari: The abundant creative energy of God is the action of God; mantra used in exercise

Hari Hari Hari Har: The flow and action of God is the creativity of God; mantra used in exercise

Hariang: Destroyer; mantra used to break blocks to prosperity

Higher Triangle: Chakras 5, 6 and 7

Indra: Hindu god of the heavens

Japji: Literally recitation for the Soul; the Sikh morning prayer

Kabir: A 15th Century Indian saint and poet of Muslim heritage, but also claimed by Hindus

Kriya: Literally, completed action; an exercise or a group of exercises leading to a specific effect

Kundal: Coil of hair from one's beloved

Kundalini: Coil of energy; raising the kundalini develops all latent talents and potentials

Laya Yoga: Meditation practice that uses the rhythmic coordination of manta and application of the locks to create the experience of ecstasy

Lower Triangle: Chakras 1, 2 and 3

Mala: Rosary

Mantra: A repeated mind-altering sound

Mool: Root

Mudra: Hand position

Neck Lock: Pulling the chin in a bit so that the neck is in line with the rest of the spine and so that the head is held steady with the face and neck relaxed; allows energy to flow to the higher centers; always used during meditation unless otherwise specified

Nittri: Eyes

Ong Naamo Guru Dayv Naamo: I call upon the Creator, I call upon Divine Wisdom; mantra used for tuning in

Ong Namo Guroo Dayv Namo Guroo Dayv Namo Guroo Dayv-aa: I call upon the Creator, I call upon Divine Wisdom, I call upon Divine Wisdom, Divine Wisdom: mantra used for guidance, for aligning with the Soul and releasing the ego's games

Ong So Hang: Creator, I Am That; mantra for the heart chakra

Pauri: Stanza; part of a larger poetic composition

Prana: Life force energy

Pranayam: Yogic breathing exercises

Pranic Body: The Body of life force energy carried on the breath

Prasaad: Gift or blessing

Root Lock: Done by pulling up on the anal sphincter muscle and sex organ and at the same time pulling in on the navel; moves excess lower chakra energy to the higher centers; stimulates creativity, inner security, empowerment and self-healing; not recommended for pregnant or menstruating women nor pre-pubescent children

Saa Ray Saa Saa, Saa Ray Saa Saa, Saa Ray Saa Saa Saa Rang, Har Ray Har Har, Har Ray Har Har, Har Ray Har Har, Har Ray Har Har Har Rang: That Infinite Totality is here, everywhere. That creativity of God is here, everywhere; mantra used to open the chakras, also used for prosperity, protection and good luck

Saa Taa Naa Maa: Loosely translated, the Infinite takes form which dies and is reborn; mantra of regeneration, used in meditation and exercise; Laya Yoga variation of Sat Naam

Sadhana: Spiritual practice

Sahaj: Effortless flow; slow; an easy path to happines and bliss

Sat Naam: Literally, Truth Name; mantra frequently in kundalini yoga, both as an inner focus during exercise and for meditation

Sat Naam Waa Hay Guru: Literally, Truth Name Wow! Indescribable Ecstasy Wisdom; mantra linking the Truth with the ecstasy of God, usually used in meditation

Seva: Selfless service

Shabad: Literally, word; in practice, a hymn that functions like a mantra

Shabad Guru: Hymns that lock the ecstasy of consciousness into the psyche when they are recited or sung

Shabad Yoga: The technology of using shabads to create specific changes in consciousness

Shakti: Feminine Creative Power of the Universe

Shuni Mudra: Mudra for patience, discipline and purity of consciousness; the tip of the thumb touches the tip of the middle finger

Shunia: Stillpoint; the state of consciousness in which the ego is zeroed out

Siri Guru Granth Sahib: The Sikh Guru, also known as the Shabad Guru; scriptures that lock the ecstasy of consciousness into the psyche when recited or sung

Sitali: Cooling

Subagh: Good fortune

Sukh: Peace, happiness and comfort

Surya: Sun

Surya Mudra: Mudra for health, creativity and energy; the tip of the thumb touches the tip of the ring finger (Sun finger)

3HO: Healthy, Happy, Holy Organization; the organization that promotes Kundalini Yoga and related activities

Tithe: Giving 10% to God

Waa-hay Guru Waa-hay Guru Waa-hay Guru Waa-hay Jeeo: An untranslatable mantra that connects the indescribable ecstasy of God with the ecstasy of the Soul; mantra used to connect with the Soul

Yoga: Union or yoke; activities that promote the experience of Oneness

BIBLIOGRAPHY

Bhajan, Yogi. (1997) K.R.I. International Teacher Training Certification Level I Manual. Espanola, NM. Kundalini Research Institute.

Bhajan, Yogi. (1997) Owner's Manual for the Human Body. Los Angeles. Kundalini Research Institute.

Bhajan, Yogi. (1982) Relax & Rejoice: A Marriage Manual, vol. 2. Pomona, CA. Kundalini Research Institute.

Bhajan, Yogi. (1995) Self-Knowledge. Espanola, NM. Ancient Healing Ways.

Bhajan, Yogi. (1980) Survival Kit: Meditations and Exercises for Stress and Pressure of the Times. Espanola, NM. Ancient Healing Ways.

Bhajan, Yogi. (1997) The Master's Touch: On Being a Sacred Teacher for the New Age. Los Angeles. Kundalini Research Institute.

Duggal, K.S. (1993) Sikh Gurus: Their Lives & Teachings. New Delhi. UBS Publishers' Distributors Ltd.

Friedman, Philomena C. (January 1996) "The Uses of Adversity." House Beautiful, vol. 138, #1, p.15.

Kaur, Bibiji Inderjit, compiler. The Psyche of the Golden Shield: Treasures of the Sikh Scriptures. Los Angeles. This is the best source for shabads for prosperity.

Khalsa, Atma Singh, and Khalsa, Guruprem Kaur. (2001) A Year with the Master: Meditations for the New Millennium: 2000. Santa Cruz, NM. Yoga Gems. This is actually a CD-Rom.

Khalsa, Guruchander Singh, D.C. (1993) Numerology. Santa Fe, NM. Radiant Light Press.

Bibliography

Khalsa, Gururattan Kaur, Ph.D., and Maxwell, Ann Marie. (1988) Relax and Renew. Coronado, CA. Yoga Technology Press.

Khalsa, Gururattan Kaur, Ph.D., and Maxwell, Ann Marie. (1988) Transitions to a Heart-Centered World. Coronado, CA. Yoga Technology Press.

Khalsa, Manjit Kaur, Ed.D., and Khalsa, Siri Tapa Kaur. (1996) Radiance and Victory: A Woman's Way to Prosperity. The Radiant Woman Press. Most of the sets and meditations in this manual work equally well for men and women.

Khalsa, Sardar Singh. (Winter 1988) "3HO Europe: the '70's and '80's." Beads of Truth, vol. 2, bead no. 21, p. 3.

Khalsa, Shakta Kaur. (2001) Kundalini Yoga: Unlock Your Inner Potential Through Life-Changing Exercise. New York. Dorling Kindersley Publishing, Inc.

Khalsa, Shakti Parwha Kaur. (1996) Kundalini Yoga: The Flow of Eternal Power. New York. Penguin Putnam, Inc.

Khalsa, Subagh Singh. (1997) The Success of the Soul: A Guide to Peace, Purpose and Prosperity. Boston. Charles E. Tuttle Co., Inc.

Khalsa, Tarn Taran Kaur. (Winter 1988) "Hamburg." Beads of Truth, vol. 2, bead no. 21, p. 6.

K.R.I. Kundalini Meditation Manual for Intermediate Students. Eugene, OR. Ancient Healing Ways.

K.R.I. (1976) Kundalini Yoga Manual. Pomona, CA. K.R.I. Publications.

K.R.I. (1976) Kundalini Yoga/Sadhana Guidelines. Los Angeles. Arcline Publications.

K.R.I. (1989) The Inner Workout Manual. Los Angeles. Arcline Publications.

K.R.I. (1984) Yoga for the 80's. Pomona, CA. Arcline Publications.

Lalli, Frank. (January 1996) "How She Turned $5000 into $22 Million (and how you might too...)." Money, vol. 138, #1, p.64.

Shabad Kirtan: The Songs and Hymns of Sikh Dharma. Los Angeles.

Takhar, Gurkirat Singh. (1997) The History of Sikhism (Guru Nanak Dev to Guru Gobind Singh). Surrey, BC, Canada. Kirpal Singh Dhaliwal.

RESOURCES

For Books, Tapes, CDs, Videos & Yogi Teas:
Ancient Healing Ways
PO Box 130
Espanola NM 87532
Phone: 1-800-359-2940 or (505) 747-2860
Fax: (505) 747-2868
Email: ahwc@cybermesa.com
www.a-healing.com

Cherdi Kala
436 N. Bedford Drive #308
Beverly Hills, CA 90210
Phone and fax: (310) 838-9989
Email: simran@cherdikala.com
www.cherdikala.com

To Locate a KRI Certified Kundalini Yoga Teacher Near You:
International Kundalini Yoga Teachers Association
4 Shady Lane
Espanola NM 87532
Phone: (505) 753-0423
Fax: (505) 753-5982
Email: ikyta@3ho.org
www.kundaliniyoga.com

For 3HO Events and Information
Website has Yogi Bhajan Articles:
3HO Foundation
Phone: 1-888-346-2420 or (505) 753-4988
Fax: (505) 753-1999
Email: yogainfo@3ho.org
www.3ho.org

Sikh Dharma Dasvandh Publishes Prosperity Paths

Website Has Lots of Prosperity Articles, Techniques and Meditations
A Place to Tithe:
Sikh Dharma Dasvandh
PO Box 249
Santa Cruz NM 87567
Phone: (505) 747-0388
Fax: (505) 753-5973
Email: dasvandh@sikhdharma.org
www.dasvandh.org

To Contact Yogi Bhajan:

Yogi Bhajan
01A Ram Das Guru Place
Espanola NM 87532
Email: yogibhajan@3ho.org
www.yogibhajan.com

To Contact Siri Kirpal Kaur Khalsa:

Email: skirpal@open.org

To Contact the Yogi Tea Company:

In the US and Canada:
Golden Temple
PO Box 1197
Santa Cruz NM 87567
or: 2545 Prairie Road
Eugene OR 97402
Phone: 1-800-YOGI-TEA
www.goldentemple.com

For Herbal Advice:
wellmasters@goldentemple.com
In Europe:
KIT B.V.
Oosteinde 5
1017 WT Amsterdam
The Netherlands
Phone: 3120-420-77-34
Fax: 3120-624-22-53
Email: info@goldentemple.nl
www.yogitea.nl

A Few Useful Websites:
www.childrensyoga.com
www.kundaliniyoga.org
www.realworldenlightenment.com
www.sikhnet.com
www.cyberzones.com/amritnivas

To Contact Yogi Ji Press:
Yogi Ji Press
PO Box 970
Santa Cruz NM 87567
Phone: 1-888-809-0885 or (505) 753-5086
Fax: (505) 753-9249
Email: nam@newmexico.com

Also From Yogi Ji Press

P.O. Box 970A Santa Cruz, NM 87567

Tel 505-753-5086 Fax 505-753-9249

e-mail:nam@newmexico.com

Contact us to be on our mailing list and to receive a catalog.

Sacred Sexual Bliss
A Technology for Ecstasy
by Sat-Kaur Khalsa, Ed.D.
ISBN#0-9655523-2-2 228pp. $19.95

The intent of this book is to help people release and heal their guilt about sex, uplift their consciousness about sex, and expand their knowledge about sex. From this foundation, couples can build confidence, security, and trust with each other and bridge the gap between sexuality and spirituality. Sex can truly become an experience of Divine Bliss.

The Art of Making Sex Sacred
Techniques for Intimate Relationships
by GuruTerath Kaur Khalsa, Ph.D.
ISBN#0-9-655523-1-4 144pp. $19.95

Based on the teachings of Kundalini Yoga Master Yogi Bhajan, Ph.D
It includes Kundalini Yoga exercises, meditations and kriyas for male potency and female radiance. There is a large section of fully illustrated and documented Venus Kriyas(special meditative yoga exercises done in couples) and meditations for couples.

Guru for the Aquarian Age:
The Life and Teachings of Guru Nanak
ISBN#0-9655523-0-6 132pp. $12.95

The timeless story of this 15th century Indian saint and founder of the Sikh religion is full of humor and wisdom. Guru Nanak's story inspires us to have the courage to meet the test of these times.